Tithes of Blood

by
Billy Ellis

Henry Martin Wilkins and Davy Crockett Wilkins
Co. E "The Prairie Gurards" 11th Miss. Vol. Infantry
Killed in the Pickett/Pettigrew charge at Gettysburg, July 3, 1863

Tithes of Blood
A Confederate Soldier's Story

by
Billy Ellis

Southern Heritage Press
4035 Emerald Drive
Murfreesboro, Tennessee 37130

First printing 1997.

Library of Congress Cataloging-in-Publication Data.

Ellis, Billy 1940 -
Tithes of Blood: A Confederate Soldier's Story
Includes maps and illustrations

ISBN 1-889332-12-7

Library of Congress Number
97-067003

Published
by
Southern Heritage Press
4035 Emerald Drive
Murfreesboro, Tennessee 37130

Dedicated to the Confederate Private

Especially

My Great Grandfather
Pvt. Thomas J. Wilkins
Co. E, "The Prairie Guards"
11th Mississippi Infantry
Lee's Army of Northern Virginia

and his Granddaughter and my mother,

Sarah Elizabeth Wilkins Ellis

They kept the faith of men and saints,
sublime and pure and bright!

TITHES OF BLOOD

About the Author

Billy Ellis is a native of Lexington, Mississippi, where he serves as chairman of the board of the Holmes County Bank.

His intense interest in the Civil War was kindled by his high school English teacher, Margie Riddle Bearss, and her husband Ed Bearss, both famous Civil War historians. The author's special interest in Co. E, "The Prairie Guards", 11th Mississippi Infantry, was nurtured by his mother, along with Tom White Crigler, the former commander-in-chief of the Sons of Confederate Veterans.

The author served as color Sergeant of the University Greys drill team while he attended Ole Miss during the Civil War Centennial.

Billy currently serves as board member and art chairman of the 11th Mississippi Memorial Committee and he is a proud member of the Bonnie Blue Literary Society of the Sons of Confederate Veterans.

The author is a respected outdoor writer/bow hunter, and his first book, *Hunter to the Dawn,* was successful.

Billy Ellis is a guardian of the undaunted spirit of the 11th Mississippi.

TABLE OF CONTENTS

Acknowledgments

To Margie and Ed Bearss, Noted Civil War historians,
for their guidance, encouragement and technical
assistance.

To my three children, Heather Ellis Sellers, Alyssa
Ellis and Scott Ellis for their love and support - they care.

To Dr. Hubert McAlexander - University of Georgia
and Dr. Tom McCraw - Harvard University,
my Ole Miss pals who taught me
more than they will ever know.

~~~~~

My Appreciation for technical assistance goes to my kinsmen
in the Thomas J. Wilkins family for sharing their manuscripts,
photographs and oral history relating to the Civil War period.
Especially helpful were Tom Wilkins' grandchildren: Sarah
Elizabeth Wilkins Ellis, Dorothy Wilkins Fraley, Louise Wilkins
Anderson, T. J. Wilkins, Bill Wilkins and cousins Joe T. Wilkins
III, Abbey Franks, Jimmy and Joe Anderson and Mary Alice
Stewart.

Archival assistance was rendered by Mary Bess Paluzzi,
Assistant Librarian at the Lowndes County Library; Ann
Ellison, Librarian and custodian of the Foose Civil War Library
founded by Don Barrett and located in the Lexington Public
Library.

TITHES OF BLOOD

Dr. David Sansing, history professor emeritus at Ole Miss and his fellow historians, Starke Miller and Steve Stubbs, who shared their important data on the 11th Mississippi, especially "The University Greys". To Scott Hartwig, Park Historian at Gettysburg, and Terry Winschel, Park Superintendent at Vicksburg, for sharing their extensive knowledge of the Pickett/Pettigrew charge. To Grady Howell, Mississippi's distinguished Civil War author for sharing pertinent documents and photographs with me. To Gettysburg's artist-in-residence, Dale Gallon, and his chief historian, Wayne Motts, who both added timely artistic and historical content to this book. To Hosea Grisham for teaching me how to assimilate the above information. To Mike Steen and Brenda Holley Farmer for manuscript preparation. To Gib Ford for the dust-jacket lay-out. To Brother Will Campbell for validating the southern ethos of this book. To the devoted men and women of the 11th Mississippi Memorial Committee for memorializing our gallant heroes in grey. Dr. David Sansing, Chairman; Ex-Governor William Winter, Ex Officio Chairman; and U. S. Senator Thad Cochran, Honorary Chairman

Members: Bob Alexander, Murray Avent, Michael Ballard, Michael Beard, Gage Black, Billy Ross Brown, Walker Coffey, Howard Duvall, Jr., The Author, Gray Evans, Hunter Gholson, Elbert Hilliard, Will Lewis Jr., Scott Long, Wallace McMillan, Starke Miller, Willie Morris, Andrew Mullins Jr., Steve Stubbs, Joseph T. Wilkins III, Kenneth Williams and Terry Winschel.

IX

TITHES OF BLOOD

Addendum to the Reader

All of the events and names of the soldiers involved in the valorous history of the 11th Mississippi Infantry Regiment are real. Some of the narration and dialog, however, is my own.

This is an actual account of the courageous deeds of simple country boys. I have a sacred trust with their precious memory which I can never betray.

Billy Ellis

TITHES OF BLOOD

FOREWORD

We are the stuff of stars, quickened by the breath of God. Since our heritage is the heavens, we are often moved by the epic deeds and selfless courage of mere mortals who somehow seem charged by some cosmic energy.

In the tangled memory of my own genes are certain atoms that surged up Cemetery Hill at Gettysburg when they first resided in my great-grandfather, Thomas J. Wilkins, Co. E, 11th Mississippi Infantry.

These atoms in me cry out for answers to the eternal question; how starving, sick, ragged, wounded, husks of men could rise above their abject state of degradation to acts of valor unprecedented in the annals of human history?

I have plowed through reams of research material, compiled my family's oral history and plumbed the depths of my own soul for clues to this eternal riddle. The answers do not come easily; they come in bits and sketches such as this excerpt from Tom Wilkins' diary:

"I dug a peas of my pants leg and a big peas of cloged blud out of my wond. I am in hopes I will get better now in a few days. I am suffering a great deal but I feal very thankful to God for his kind care and keeping through my affliction. Thou I am a long ways from home God is with me. My wond feals some better but my foot gibes me some trouble."

Thomas J. Wilkins, Esq.
Brooksville, Miss.

I 'feal' much better for having chronicled the epic deeds of these brave and selfless heroes of the Thin Grey Line.

Billy Ellis

Indian Bluffs
Lexington, Mississippi

Prologue

As a child in the forties, I would always accompany my paternal grandparents to the Mississippi Gulf coast each Summer. Our conveyance was a bulbous four-door Dodge sedan full of fried chicken, stuffed eggs, iced tea, and a wide eyed school boy full of great anticipation. We always left at dawn and we usually arrived to see the evening sun setting over the Gulf of Mexico at Biloxi, Mississippi.

Every summer we would park in front of Beauvoir, President Jefferson Davis' last home. The setting sun turned the lovely columned veranda to gold, a true monument to by-gone antebellum days.

But that was not why we stopped. Across the expansive gallery, framed by wind-gnarled live oaks, was a long row of hand-made, hickory high-backed rocking chairs, occupied by gaunt, venerable looking men with skin the color of their hickory chairs and pure white hair and beards that hung down to their belt buckles. In the setting sun their countenance took on a golden spectral glow reminiscent of primeval Celtic warrior-priests come back only briefly to take the ocean air. They merely rocked and stared out to sea, imperturbable in their cadence and measure. I stared at them in slack-jawed amazement.

Big Daddy broke my reverie. "Those are the Confederate Veterans," he announced. "Wh-Wh-Who?" I stammered. "Those men fought bravely in our war for Southern independence many years ago," he answered.

The evening breeze was picking up now and it gently ruffled their delicate spun-gold beards into intricate patterns of movement in the hazy twilight.

In my childlike wonder, I was merely content to view these priceless human treasures but now I constantly reproach myself for not having had the presence of mind to merely stroll up the old brick walk of Beauvoir and shake their dear gnarled hands; then sit on the gallery with them and hear first-hand their glorious tales of valor.

Perhaps to merely view these ancient messengers from another era was enough, maybe Keats *was* right, "heard melodies

Thomas J. Wilkins and wife, Sarah Glover Wilkins on their fiftieth wedding anniversary

XIII

are sweet, but those unheard are sweeter". This must sustain me for each June vacation revealed more vacant spaces in the long row of rocking chairs until one solitary summer all the chairs were empty. They merely rocked in the gulf breeze while the ancient live oaks soughed a gentle whisper . . . REMEMBER!

Prelude to War
Chapter I

An eerie lull enveloped the killing ground but the acrid powder smoke made each sobbing breath an ordeal. Through the skeleton-clawed branches of the tortured trees a forlorn ray of sunlight pierced the gloom and fixed in horror the sightless, staring eyes of the Yankee corpses that we had piled up for breastworks down here in this awful wilderness, completely surrounded by Hancock's corps and estranged from God and General Lee

Colonel Stone limped bravely down the line. "They'll be back boys," he cautioned, "so make every shot count!" Me and my two brothers planned to do just that with the dozen Yankee Springfields we had just collected out in no-man's-land. They would load and I would shoot. With a violent ripping sound, the deadly bees hummed over our heads once again and the gut shuddering crash of spherical case shot filled the torpid air. "They're coming!" someone yelled and I could see small patches of dark motion flitting to and fro among the shattered tree trunks and ground smoke. Bent over in a furtive crouch an enemy soldier came into my line of fire. Through my Enfield's buckhorn sights I took a fine bead on his shiny eagle breastplate and gently squeezed the trigger. When the powder smoke lifted, I saw a crumpled-up pile of blue where a live boy once stood. My brother Charlie handed me a loaded Springfield and the blood orgy continued while the Yanks kept on coming.

The whip and rattle of grape shot sang in the tree tops and the shrill flutter of parrot shells turned the whole sky into a canopy of death when a huge concussion blew me skyward and I was floating away, away back to Noxubee County, Mississippi.

> *They were fine and fair and thought themselves brave and they looked upon the coming storm with the convoluted optimism of the very young.*

The smell of honeysuckle filled the air with cloying sweetness while dogwood and azalea blooms formed a brilliant tableau behind the eighty seven earnest young soldiers who stood at attention on the Crawford, Mississippi parade ground on April 27th, 1861.

On a bunting-draped podium in front of the company, stood a portly man of thirty-eight. His pale complexion and elegant aloofness bespoke of his station in the antebellum landed gentry. His smart grey uniform was immaculate, from the black "Jeff Davis" hat with the up-turned left brim, to the intricate gold braid on his coat sleeves.

Captain W. W. Humphries intoned: "Men of the Prairie Guards, I am extremely honored today to muster you all into the official military service of our beloved State of Mississippi. I congratulate you on your military bearing, your handsome uniforms, and your superior drilling ability. Because of this, a special thanks is due your Captain, J. T. W. Hairston, who

TITHES OF BLOOD

I understand is a recent graduate of the Virginia Military Institute. I am told that this unit has become a special pet of the ladies of this community. As a token of their appreciation of your patriotism, they have sold pies and cakes to purchase the finest material with which they have sewn this lovely bonnie blue flag with '*Prairie Guards*' embroidered upon it."

Captain Humphries then handed the flag to Pleas Goolsby who hooked it to the company guidon staff and then snapped to attention. Pleas' Adam's apple twitched excitedly and he broke into a pompous grin as if the flag was actually his.

The captain continued, "This momentous day we unfurl this flag to the glad breezes that fan these broad prairies of East Mississippi. This new flag is unlike the flag under which our fathers fought British oppression; to us it is a new banner in the sky. Our old stars and stripes not only ceases to protect our lives and property, it now floats over seventy-five thousand troops marshalled to carry fire and sword into the homes of our families and kindred. With strong hearts, though sad, we, and our mothers too, are ready to say farewell to the old flag and send forth our sons to battle for constitutional liberty under this 'Bonnie Blue Flag', our new and unstained banner."

Captain Humphries then stepped down off the podium to be replaced by our local minister, Rev. W. C. Hearn, who continued: "Let us pray. . .God of our fathers, God of Liberty, and God of Battle, shield these men as they trek down unknown paths to smite the demon Goths who even now pollute our sacred Southern soil. We earnestly pray that this holy war for Southern Independence will soon be over and it shall be the northern foeman and not a single member of this company who offers up tithes of blood upon the altar of Southern Independence!"

An ant was crawlin' around the top of Davy's collar; if that critter drops down his neck and starts stinging he could get in a heap of trouble. We were standing at full attention and the old preacher was rambling on and on. When he finally got to tithes of blood, all I could think about was that ant raisin' a blood whelp on Davy's neck. We were all mighty glad when he finally said, "amen", while Davy smacked his neck, and we toted our new flag on a march around the parade ground. Man, our buttons like to have busted we were so proud, especially when the band struck up the Bonnie Blue Flag!

We Wilkins boys **did** look natty. Mr. Harrison Johnston, a tailor from Columbus, made our uniforms from some heavy cotton serge. Our belts, straps, packs, cartridge boxes and tin canteens were sent here from the central commissary in Atlanta. Our black "Jeff Davis" hats came from the militia supply depot in Jackson and we turned up the left brim and pinned it up with a big brass star that we got from the Brooksville general store. The star matched the big white star on our bonnie blue company battle flag. Our 1855 model 58 caliber U. S. percussion rifles with Maynard tape primers came from the arms depot in Jackson. We wore brogan work shoes that Daddy bought from Uncle Doc's general store in town.

TITHES OF BLOOD

After the mustering in ceremony we had a splendid dinner given in our honor at the First Baptist Church in Crawford. Liberty Martin allowed as how they always fatten up a steer fore they send it off to slaughter.

Miss Clara Shields rose to the occasion to give us a stirring speech, "Riflemen! - True sons of the South, we, her daughters, have heard born upon breezes which have hitherto breathed of naught but peace the voice of the spirit-stirring drums, the ear-piercing fife - have seen the glitter of steel which may be deemed as heralding symbols of sanguinary war. Though our hearts may be bowed down as we listen to sounds so discordant and our eyesight dimmed as we gaze upon scenes so fearfully dazzling; yet there is a spirit ever hovering not far distant which, though it puts on an air of mournful respect as if loath to disturb us in our anxious reveries, has a fascinating influence to which one seems compelled to yield - it charms while it saddens. Yes, the all-powerful spirit of Southern patriotism has triumphed - has caused our hearts to respond to yours - has given us courage to assemble here, for the purpose of presenting to you a banner, which, if destined to wave over your heads in the field of battle, we tender to you with feelings somewhat akin to those of the Spartan mother, as she gave the shield to her son, in days of yore. Accept it as a token of our respect and admiration, as a pledge of our faith in your chivalry and patriotism."

"If stern duty calls you from our midst, we will endeavor to allow our palpitating hearts to be lulled to rest, by the

5

mellow voice of the siren hope, which sings to us of a future day of glory; of a golden age to be allotted to our sunny land, which shall remain untarnished, of a time when the balmy gales and murmuring waters will unite in the joyous song of peace, peace to her children - of a time when, as we look aloft and gaze upon her quiet skies, we will number ourselves among God's chosen people, and feel that He will be with us even unto the end. Remember, when wandering far from us, as you gaze upon this standard, that these our most brilliant hopes, become our fondest prayers."

Then the local school girls' choir serenaded us with a beautiful song called *The Volunteers Welcome Home.*

Next on the agenda, our friend Rev. W. C. Hearn of Crawford, a highly gifted orator not unknown to fame, was again introduced to the audience, whom he held spell-bound with his eloquence for a short while.

Next to the podium stepped our own Captain Hairston who also made some appropriate and happy remarks, by request of the audience, in his own plain, eloquent and manly style, which brought repeated rounds of applause.

I was getting slightly bored by all this palaver and my eyes strayed to a lovely little green-eyed girl of about sixteen standing on the back row of the girls' choir. Pleas Goolsby whispered her name to me, "Liz Glover". I sure hoped she would not spurn my advances when I got back home from the war.

Next in order came dinner. A magnificent table was set in the church yard where all repaired for refreshments. A bountiful supply of everything that was good was prepared in a manner to do credit to the taste of the good and clever people of Crawford and every attention was given by our kind friends whose politeness told for them a better tale than can my humble description.

As soon as we finished the meal we mounted our mules and raced and whooped and hollered all the way to "Sunnyside", our 300 acre place that Mama had named and Papa had cleared himself. We lived in a great big dog-trot log house that had purple wisteria growin' all over the roof. It shore looked purty that evenin' with the sun settin'. Mama was standing on the front porch holdin' a bowl of half-shelled butter beans when we rode up. She looked like she had been cryin'.

We Wilkins boys enjoyed each other's company and our favorite sport was hog hunting in the swamps around Carpenter's Lake, an oxbow of the Noxubee River.

Our last hunt before the war was our most exciting. Me and my four brothers rode our mules down to the lake with our whimpering Catahoula hounds frolicking about the mules' hooves. Just as daylight filtered through the Spanish moss hung cypress trees, our lead dog Capn', a three-legged feist, opened up on a hot trail with his little bell-tinkly bark. The loss of a back leg to a huge tusker the year before had not dimmed his love of the fray. The other hounds soon joined in the chase in a wild, baying, roiling race down the far bank of the lake. We occasionally caught sight of a monster boar with a badly tattered right ear that we had already named Ole

PRELUDE TO WAR

Abe and which we had run many times with great damage to our hounds but had never brought to bay.

"Let's swim the horses acrost!" yelled Davy. "No, there's too many alligators," I retorted, and we raced around the back end of the lake. Half-way around, we heard the bell-like barking and moiling howls of the hounds and squeals, grunts and teeth clacks and we knew that the boar had bayed. We tied our mules. Since I was the oldest, they looked to me for orders, "John T., you grab Capn' and get him back out of the way." I really wanted to get Mama's *baby* away from that boar too. "Charlie, you and Henry go around to the right, I'll go left." We all circled the terrific brawl. Dogs were darting all around bawling at the top of their lungs.

Then I saw him! Ole Abe looked like a creature from the Book of Revelation. Coal black, with huge chest and hackles standing straight up, little red beady eyes and bone-white tusks that looked like railroad spikes. Those fiery eyes missed nothing and he charged out again and again at the nearest dogs with "harrumpt", "harrumpt", a primal sound which exploded from his lower chest every time he slashed at the hounds with his sickle- shaped tusks.

We were very careful not to fire toward each other, but when I finally got an opening to shoot into the hog's vitals, I raised Papa's ole flintlock and pulled the trigger. Click-BOOM, white powder smoke filled my field of view and when I ducked around the acrid cloud the huge boar had vanished for a second. An instant later, I saw a huge black blob emerge from behind a tree and charge Davy. Davy

8

turned to run, his boot caught in a saw-briar vine and he sprawled ass-over-teakettle into a mud bank, ramming his rifle barrel down in the mud. When Davy turned to face his attacker he screamed! The huge boar was just a few yards from ripping him to shreds. Right when the boar opened his mouth "harrumpt", click-BOOM, Henry's capped musket roared and the huge boar slid stone dead into Davy's still vine caught leg! "Whew!" exclaimed Davy, "I wish that had been a Yankee!"

When we got home with the huge tusker, Mama and Papa had a wild boar Barbecue and Daddy's freeman, Jim Henly, did the cooking. It was one heck of a fine going-a-way party.

After it was over, me and Davy and Charlie and Henry carved our names on the gnarled old catalpa tree that stood beside the smoke house.

Tom Wilkins, Davy Wilkins, Charlie Wilkins, Henry Wilkins - The Prairie Guards, April 3, 1861.

Staging For Battle
Chapter II

With mournful whistle screaming, our beloved "Doodle Bug" was switched onto the siding at the Crawford station on May 11, 1861.

The expectant crowd was showered with soot, cinders, and finally a monumental expulsion of steam as if the engineer had wrested deep into the very bowels of the infernal machine to produce the maximum effect for the assemblage.

Each member of the Prairie Guards stood with their families for their last leave taking. Thoughts unspoken were as heavy as the stifling air.

Captain J. T. W. Hairston stood aloof near the first passenger car with his aging mother, apprehensive about his first command and unconsciously exemplifying the old officer adage that 'familiarity breeds contempt'.

Our Wilkins family stood close together, saying nothing and trying to avoid each others eyes. Our Mama, Elizabeth Wilkins, about to have four sons ripped from her the second time since birth, stood in a kind of resigned fog that, if provoked, could quickly turn into a plunging cataract. Her baby, John Tyson, who was underage for enlistment stood sadly by her side.

"You boys take care of yourselves, don't sleep in wet clothes and don't forget to take that croton oil I gave ya if ya'll get sick. Write ifen you can..." And then it all caught up in the high part of her chest and she turned and walked slowly back to the wagon, shoulder shaking sobs muffled in her Afghan shawl.

Our Daddy, Captain Richard Wilkins, held each boy's hand in both of his, had something important to say to each of us, but nothing came out. Then he also turned away, shrugging his shoulders in a Pilate-like gesture of a man crushed by historical events beyond his control.

"ATTEN-HUT" barked J. T. W. Hairston. His Hardees Drill Manual deserted him at that moment, so he finished the order with, "Mount the train!" "Shag it or board it?!" yelled old Toad Hopper, the town drunk. Amid the tumult and tears, a few of the more perceptive soldiers heard old Frank's derisive cry and the train chugged out of the station amid sorrowful wails mixed with incongruous howls of laughter. The inadvertent perpetrator, Captain Hairston, brooded with crimson complexion in his self-inflicted misery.

The troop train roared and rocked its clickedy-clack rhythm on the north-bound journey from Columbus to Corinth, Mississippi. The scenery slid by in a monotonous patchwork of newly plowed black prairie dirt squares interspersed with green pole-fenced pastures dotted with an occasional white limestone outcropping.

When the train stopped for switching a few miles south of Okolona, I viewed a tender scene that made me homesick already. Up on a high broad prairie knoll was a sturdy and comfortable farm house with a simple tin shed roof, long galleries all around the house and well-proportioned chimneys on each side. A line of gnarled and ancient blue cedars lined the brick walk. Lavender wisteria grew up their age-silvered trunks and seas of daffodils danced in the prairie wind.

A family reunion was obviously in progress, just like we had at Sunnyside. Women in plain everyday gingham dresses with starched white full length aprons bustled about serving the family members on the freshly clipped lawn. Lean well-tanned men with gnarled hands, honest faces and pronounced Adam's apples sat apart, probably discussing either the war or the price of hogs but the butcher takes them all.

Lightening bugs soon came out and I watched them twinkle like tiny spirits in the inchoate dusk while locusts rent the air with their monotonous rasp of sound.

The young men of army age are whispering to their girl friends, giggling coyly in their yellow and blue calico dresses; girls who they may never see again. Most of the picnickers are eating fried chicken, potato salad and corn bread washed down with fresh buttermilk. Freshly baked chess pie was even then being cut for dessert.

"There is a palpable warmth and love at that place, a place of peace like Sunnyside, another place worth fighting for," Rev. Love opined.

My brother Davy had been watching too, "The idea, a bunch of Yankees coming down here and destroying our homes and way of life!" "At least we'll have 'um whipped good and proper in a couple of months!"

The train lurched into motion with ear splitting clashings

of slack couplings, whistle screams, and our reverie was broken.

The initial excitement of the journey gradually melded into monotony as one by one the young soldiers nodded off into upright, head-jiggling sleep.

Just after dawn the engineer hit his whistle twice to notify the Corinth switchman that he was inbound. The Prairie Guards began to stir, with sandy eyes and sour mouths. In ten minutes we were on the siding and collecting our gear around the baggage car.

View on the railway, looking north-west from the Corinth Depot.
From a war-time photograph

The newly elected officers tried out their new authority by squaring up the mass of men and equipment. While we were thus occupied, another company marched into the staging area. The men were all done up in the finest outfits with grey frock coats with red frogging, trousers with red stripes up the side and black felt hats pinned up on three sides with horse-hair cockades.

14

To top it all off, the men wore red-lined capes! If that ain't enough the company was followed by a large group of support personnel. "Who in thunder is you all?" inquired one of our men. "The University Greys!" came the proud reply. "What university?" "University of Mississippi!" they boasted.

Future University Greys of the University of Mississippi on the Lyceum steps

We prairie boys hadn't ever seen a man wearing a cape before. Some of the 'Greys' seemed a bit over-educated and most of these planter aristocrats also had their little darkey man-servants with them. After we had all shared the privations of war, however, we all became brothers.

The other company from Oxford, the Lamar Rifles, was named for the ole tongue-twister himself, Lucious Quintious Cinncinattus Lamar. Most of these boys were a bit different from the Greys; they were, on the whole, working class boys

15

STAGING FOR BATTLE

Members of the University Greys included Calvin B. McCaleb (left), First Lieutenant of the Corps, who enlisted on April 26, 1861; and William Handy, private, (right) who enlisted on June 1, 1862, at Harper's Ferry.

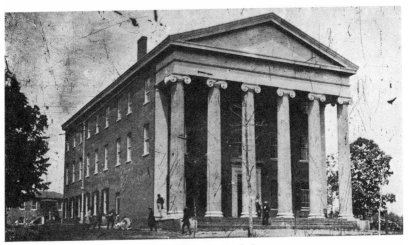

University of Mississippi's Lyceum

like us with only a few doctors, lawyers and planters throwed in for good measure.

While there, we tried to make friends with all the other companies. We figured if we were all to fight as a unit we needed to get to know each other better.

One of the Confederacy's wealthiest companies was probably the Van Dorn Reserves of Aberdeen. Each man was furnished with a tailored uniform, a Colt revolving rifle and a purse of gold. The company also carried a war chest containing several thousand dollars.

As I said before, the most colorful company was The University Greys. Their commanding officer is Captain William B. Lowry, who is only nineteen years old, tall and lanky with a classic, handsome face. Captain Lowry is a courteous and refined gentleman, well-to-do and wealthy according to my friend Second Lt. A. J. Ledbetter of our company. Ledbetter became friends with Lowry since they were fellow officers and all, plus, they both love horses and dogs. In fact, Captain Ledbetter claims that Captain Lowry brought to the university with him his bird dogs, shotguns and two horses, one for himself and one for his little Negro servant who is still with him here in the Confederate Army at Corinth.

At night, after supper, we built up a huge camp fire and swapped stories of home. Naturally, us Wilkins boys told our hog hunting tales while the University Greys talked reverently about some building called the 'Lyceum' like it was some kind of 'holy of holies'. It must not have been too holy, however, since the rumor was told that the Greys Captain Lowry had ridden his horse into the building carrying a bull whip and threatened to beat Chancellor Barnard because he had tried to have Lowry expelled for neglecting his studies as well as allowing the Greys to remove their muskets from the company arsenal and use them to hunt with.

Chancellor Barnard and the faculty considered Lowery and the "Greys" a major disciplinary problem and Lowery developed a position of allegiance to the Confederate Army above his alma mater. When Barnard finally removed Lowery from the school roll for ignoring assignments and missing recitation, the "Greys" captain refused to leave. He pointed out that a captain's place was with his company. The chancellor and faculty finally acquiesced but shortly thereafter the "Greys" were mustered in on April 26th, 1861 and entrained for Corinth with their sister company from Oxford, the Lamar Rifles.

Corinth, Mississippi, was a fine town and it was well prepared for its role as a military staging area. We stayed here for a month drilling and training, as all of our companies arrived from all over the state. When all ten companies arrived we drew lots for our company letters, and Governor Pettus (mercifully) gave a short christening speech. On May 4th, 1861, we were officially designated the 11th Mississippi Regiment and were mustered in as follows:

Company A, University Greys, commissioned

at Oxford, Lafayette County, 7 February 1861

Company B, Coahoma Invincibles, mustered at Friar's Point, Coahoma County, 2 March 1861

Company C, Prairie Rifles, mustered at Okolona, Chickasaw County, 2 March 1861

Company D, Neshoba Rifles, mustered at Philadelphia, Neshoba County, 13 April 1861

Company E, Prairie Guards, mustered at Crawford, Lowndes County, 15 February 1861

Company F, Noxubee Rifles, mustered at Macon, Noxubee County, 24 February 1861

Company G, Lamar Rifles, mustered at Oxford, Lafayette County, 23 February 1861

Company H, Chickasaw Guards, mustered at Houston, Chickasaw County, 19 March 1861

Company I, Van Dorn Reserves, mustered at Aberdeen, Monroe County, 20 February 1861

Company K, Carroll County Rifles, mustered at Carrollton, Carroll County, 26 February 1861

William H Moore and Phillip F. Liddell, both gentlemen of means, were elected colonel and lieutenant colonel, respectively.

VIRGINIA BOUND

Chapter III

It was at Corinth that the individual companies of the 11th Mississippi were melded into a single cohesive fighting unit. Our commanders did this by pounding Hardees' rifle and light infantry tactics into us. Our regiment contained 10 companies from all over central Mississippi and numbered about one thousand soldiers.

Each company was commanded by a captain who was always posted at the right front rank of his company with his left elbow touching his first sergeant. The three lieutenants and sergeants were posted behind the company formation as file closers.

In combat drill we were taught to achieve combat formation anytime we heard the "long roll" on the drums. Then we were admonished not to shoot until we were within effective rifle range of the enemy; pick out a particular Yankee and aim low. When possible shoot the officers and all artillery horses first and don't forget to scream like Banshees!

Under all conditions, hold your ranks and when charging do so rapidly. Do not pause to plunder the dead and do not stop to help wounded comrades. The medical corps is set up for that and the best help you can give them is by running the Yankees off the field of battle.

Every morning at 5:00 we got up, marched or deployed

all day, went to bed, got up the next day and marched all over again. Each day at sunset, each company formed up at its respective quarters and marched out to a position on the parade field called the "color line". Company C was always in the center and carried the colors of the regiment, a position of honor as well as extreme danger during combat. "C", then, was always called the "color company" although in the confusion of battle, soldiers from other companies sometimes carried the battle flag. Company "C" formed first in the center, then companies "I", "F", "D", and "A" formed, dressing left on the flag; then marched "H", "E", "G", "K", and "B" dressing right on the colors. Once the battle formation was properly dressed while the troops are at "shoulder arms", the commanding officer ordered, "order arms" and the rifle was pulled off of the right shoulder and smartly popped into the left hand where the weapon rested diagonally across the chest. Next the order was "parade rest" which is executed by snapping the right foot back and letting the rifle drop in front of the body while the barrel rested in the crook of the left arm. Then our regimental band would crank up "Dixie" and march across the front of the battle formation. When the band cleared company "B", the companies would form into columns of four and follow the band back to our quarters.

We used this formation at the final grand review the afternoon before we left for Virginia. After the grand review, Lieutenant Hairston made us a little speech, "Men, you have acquitted yourselves admirably." "I hope acquitted is the same thing as quitten, fer we ain't quit marching fer four weeks straight," yelled my cousin, Fletch Norwood. Lieutenant Hairston bristled and tried to have him bucked and gagged, but nobody would obey his order.

While we were at Corinth, we had the election of officers. We organized the 11th Mississippi Regiment of Volunteer Infantry by electing Joe Moore, who was Captain of the Van Dorn reserves, as Colonel; P. F. Liddell, who was Captain of the Carroll Rifles, was elected Lt. Colonel, and S. F. Butler, a Private of the Prairie Guards, as Major. At the organization, the Prairie Guards became Company E of the Regiment.

From Corinth our Regiment was sent by train to Lynchburg, Virginia, where it was mustered into the service of the Confederate States of America on May 13, 1861. Leaving Lynchburg in a few days, we arrived at Strasburg, the terminus of the Manassas Gap Railroad. From this point to Winchester, our regiment was transported in troop wagons. Some of the boys criticized the Confederacy very sharply for not furnishing more comfortable conveyances for her soldiery.

Winchester, Virginia was a lovely little town of tree-lined streets, quaint shops and 4,400 people that lay at the junction of several strategic highways and a railroad. This made Winchester a hub center for movement of men and war materials. It had already been designated as headquarters of a certain local general named Tom Jackson whose only claim to fame so far was to hang some revolutionary fanatic named John Brown.

We were billeted in an old deserted flour mill that was

cold, damp, and moldy smelling. In two days, however, we were marched twenty miles over to Harper's Ferry. We reached there on May 19th. Harper's Ferry was a dirty, but interesting little town down in the bowl of the Shenandoah Mountains at the confluence of the Shenandoah and Potomac Rivers. Due to the steep slopes of the mountainous terrain, land space was at a premium and all of the houses, saloons, hotels and shops of Harper's Ferry were jammed together on three short main streets. The main industry was the armory which produced some mighty fine rifles, but which also filled the air with dirty coal smoke and soot which covered everything at Harper's Ferry.

While there we did some sight-seeing. We went to the

John Brown

Old Engine House where John Brown had started this war. At that time then-Lt. J. E. B. Stuart and then-Colonel Robert E. Lee had suppressed and captured John Brown and then turned him over to the Virginia troops commanded by Col. Thomas J. Jackson for hanging. That's what we were all about now.

TITHES OF BLOOD

Company and Regimental drills occupied most of our time here at Harper's Ferry and we trampled down many acres of fine red clover. There was also some police and outpost duty. We raised Cain until they issued us brand new 58 caliber Enfields. After a little practice, with these fine rifles we Wilkins boys could knock the stripes off a skunk at 300 yards.

Measles broke out in our camp about then and, owing to the lack of hospitals, the sick were mostly sent back to the towns along the railroads where they were cared for by the kindhearted citizens. While here Company E lost by disease: E. R. Crouch, Stephen Moorhead, J. Quik, and orderly Ed Sanders.

After the evacuation of Harper's Ferry, the Army returned to Winchester, Virginia, since intelligence had indicated that Federal Maj. Gen. Robert Patterson's army was heading our way. This march was the first march in which we carried our rifle, cartridge box, knapsack, blanket, canteen and haversack with rations. It was a tough march with all of this load. It took the greater part of three days to cover a distance of 30 miles. Ten miles a day would be totally unacceptable in a combat situation.

Gen. Thomas J. "Stonewall" Jackson

VIRGINIA BOUND

We soon returned to Winchester when the Yankee threat proved to be only a feint. Several days later we were marched out and drawn up in line of battle at Bunker Hill and loaded our guns. All night long we stood in line in the cold rain in a wheat field. Colonel Moore came down the line, shivering just like we were. He called out, "Boys, who has any whiskey?" In the darkness, many canteens clanked and we all became fully stimulated in short order. Next morning we learned that the enemy was 10 or 15 miles away at that time. After recruiting at Winchester for about two weeks we started out to reinforce Gen. Thomas J. Jackson, who was having his first battle with the enemy near Falling Waters on July 2nd.

By the time we reached Darksville, all was quiet and the Regiment returned to its old quarters. A week or so later, the 11th Mississippi was hurried out of camp to meet a reported advance of Yankees a few miles distance. The "long roll" was drummed in deadly earnest by our four little baby-faced drummer boys. We were issued two days' cooked rations which we all promptly ate. Canteens were filled and we were issued forty rounds of 58 caliber Enfield ammunition which we stowed in the tin dividers in our big leather cartridge boxes which hung by a leather strap from our necks. I always kept plenty of firing caps in the small cap box on my waist belt.

To fire our Enfield rifles, we pulled a paper wrapped cartridge from the box, bit off the tip with the powder, poured the powder in the barrel, set the 58 caliber bullet in the barrel muzzle and rammed it down with the ramrod, then put a firing cap on the nipple and waited to draw a fine bead on a Yankee.

When the dawn broke, our battle orders were given. Company E, the Prairie Guards, was detailed to support a gun of Riley's Battery. Three of our old citizens, Col. Jim Blain, Beverly Matthews, and Maj. George Hairston were visiting our Company at the time and promptly fell into ranks for the battle. Arriving on the field, we loaded our new Tower Enfields and went through the manual of arms, but in doing so, Jehu Kirksey accidentally discharged his rifle. This was regretted very much and for a long time our Company was blamed for scaring the game before it came within reach. Ole Jehu felt so bad that Captain Hairston chose not to punish him. After that, Jehu never put a cap on his rifle's nipple until the Yanks were in spittin' distance.

After this false alarm, the Regiment settled down to hard drilling. Our dress parades attracted the ladies in large numbers. From this camp, the Flag of the Prairie Guards was sent home in the care of Rev. W. C. Hearn. All of the company flags were retired and the flag adopted by Congress and known as the Stars and Bars was presented to the Regiment.

While at this place, Company E lost three men, John Durry died in agony with the whooping cough, B. Whitlock and B. F. Smith were discharged.

About noon, July 19th, Johnson's Army left Winchester to reinforce Beauregard at Manassas. It was a toilsome

Brig.-Gen. Barnard E. Bee (in the uniform of a captain of infantry of the old service)

march and it was on the evening of the 20th when General Bee's Brigade reached Piedmont on the Manassas Railroad.

The Brigade, except eight companies of the 11th Mississippi, was transported by train to Manassas that night and was in the engagement the next day. On the morning of July 21st, 1861, we Prairie Guards, and the companies that were left behind took the cars, but did not arrive on the field in time to take part in the battle. When we got near the battle, the engineer on our train became scared because shells were falling close to the engine and he stopped the train. At this our colonel went up and asked him why he had stopped and he said, "Sir, I was only hired to take you up to the battle, not get involved in the battle myself." At this our Colonel got very agitated and ordered the engineer hung. We could not believe what was happening, but he ordered us to do it and we complied. The engineer was hung right there from a big oak tree by the railroad tracks. It was not a pretty thing, it was not a decent thing to watch. His eyeballs were poked out, tongue lashing around, fighting the air with a rope around his neck, screaming for his family, but he died, just like a lot of our boys were

28

going to die that very day because of his cowardly action.

In the confusion of pending battle, only two of our companies, the University Greys and the Noxubee Rifles with Lt. Col. Phillip F. Lidell commanding, quickly boarded another train and rode into action that day along with the Second Mississippi infantry regiment. Arriving on the Manassas Plain, our two companies were ordered to take up a reserve position behind the Confederate left flank along Bull Run. We were a small part of Gen. Barnard E. Bee's Brigade which also included the 2nd Mississippi along with the 4th Alabama, the 6th North Carolina and the 1st Tennessee.

Gen. Bee rallying our troops at 1st Manassas

VIRGINIA BOUND

After agonizing hours of waiting, we finally entrained for the battle. We were within earshot of the cannons when a horseman rode up and shouted to our very brave new engineer, "Stop the train, for God's sake, the Yanks have the road!" As the train squealed to a halt, all of our eight remaining companies, including our company E jumped off and scurried into battle formation. When Company B, the Coahoma Invincibles swung into line, they stirred up a bushel of the biggest bumble bees I had ever seen. Of course, it caused much scurrying, and Captain Green, of Company G, seeing our men running, and a few of his company, charged down the line, swearing at the men for running, but when a few bees popped him he just about wore out that big plume he had in his hat. It was many a day before he heard the last of it.

As the day wore on the Union General McDowell launched a major attack right at General Bee's position. In the face of withering fire and out-numbered three to one, our boys began a slow withdrawal up Henry Hill. At that moment, General Bee yelled to his brigade, "Rally behind the Virginians! They stand there like a stone wall!" and Bee's brigade, including our Companies A and F, rallied to General Jackson.

In the ensuing rout, our Mississippi boys topped a slight ridge to find the vaunted "Fire Zouaves" of New York City. Our troops pulled up, assumed firing order, and poured a deadly volley into the red pantalooned Yankees. Our companies A and F then gave a fierce rebel yell, threw down their empty Enfields, and charged with nothing more than their D-guard Bowie knives! This was simply too much for the pride of New York, and they fled in great disorder screaming, "Betrayed! Betrayed!"

After all vestige of Yankee resistance had been quelled, the trumpets sounded "recall" and our boys re-assumed regimental combat formation. It was then that they learned that our outstanding General had been killed soon after he christened General Jackson with his well earned sobriquet, "Stonewall".

As the Federal retreat became a rout, the men to the 11th Mississippi joined in rounding up the hundreds of beaten Yankees who could not get away. One of the prisoners was Brig. Gen. Orlando Wilcox. The wounded captive told our Lt. Col. Liddell how much he admired the magnificent horse he rode and offered him $1,000 in gold for the animal. Liddell thanked the general, but said that, inasmuch as the horse was a gift from the University of Mississippi, it would not do for him to sell the animal. So bemused were Liddell's men by the incident that they prevailed upon him to rename the horse "Wilcox".

As we waited forlornly in a reserve area, the University Greys and our sister unit, the Noxubee Rifles, arrived from the battle, begrimed with powder and cocky and proud to have "seen the elephant," as the Yankees call it.

They were proudly waving our big regimental "Star and Bars" battle flag, sewn by our hometown ladies at Crawford, Mississippi. Our flag was unique because instead of having the stars in a circle, they were placed like a Christian cross and the top red stripe had 11th Mississippi proudly emblazoned on it.

We didn't realize it at the time but the similarity of the Stars and Bars to the Stars and Stripes very nearly caused a disaster for our Southern Confederacy, when Gen. Kirby Smith approached the field from an unexpected quarter, General Beauregard, fearing it was the enemy's flag, was about to make preparation to retreat. The next winter, Congress adopted a new flag General Beauregard designed in place of this one. It was the Confederate battle flag that we know today; the Saint Andrew's Cross with stars.

After staying on Bull Run for a few days, the Regiment was sent to Bristoe Station. While at Bristoe Station we had lots of bad luck. There was considerable sickness in camp and Jim Knox, E. P. Linecum, and John Robinson of our Company died.

On the 15th day of October the line of the army was withdrawn to Centerville and the line was established on the Occaquan River. It was here that our worst luck so far befell us. That was when Brig. Gen. William Henry Chase Whiting became our new commander. He succeeded General Bee who was killed at First Manassas.

General Whiting was an arrogant and ill-tempered alcoholic and he was definitely not a soldier's general like, ole Joe Johnston or A. P. Hill.

11th Mississippi Regiment flying its distinctive "cross of stars" battle flag passing in review before Gen. P. G. T. Beauregard, July 21, 1861

11th Mississippi Regiment's first "Cross of Stars" battle flag sewn by the ladies of Crawford, Miss.

Winter Quarters
Chapter IV

We held the right of the long Confederate line near Dumphries, Virginia. With cold weather setting in, General Lee selected Camp Fisher as the site for the 11th Mississippi's winter quarters. This site had plenty of water and adequate drainage and fairly good transportation facilities. When General Lee tried to get us wood for the winter, however, the local planters were reluctant to lend us the services of their slaves to help us. That news made us wonder whether we were fighting the right folks or not.

At any rate, we soon commenced to making rude log huts to keep out the winter cold and damp. Since we didn't have any saws in our company, we used axes. With 40 men taking turns, we soon had a proper number of logs cut to build 10 four-man log huts. We used artillery and cavalry horses to drag the logs back to our company building area.

Then began the tedious work of notching and laying the logs. We then chinked them with clay mortar mixed with straw made from dried grass. Our walls were eight feet high and the roof beams were covered with tacked-on tent shelter halves and gum blankets. Our dirt floor was covered with a piece of canvas that, it is rumored, I "midnight requisitioned" from an engineering battalion. We got some bricks from an old mansion's chimneys that the Yankees had burned and built ourselves a nice fireplace.

WINTER QUARTERS

After building two double decker bunks and installing pegs in the logs to hold our Enfields, gear, and cooking utensils we soon had ourselves quite a presentable hut. All the boys then commenced to place name signs on their cabins.

One hut was named "Buzzard Roost", one "Rebel Rousters", one "Growlers", one "Howlers" and me and my three brothers named ours the "Boar's Nest" since we were all hog hunters at heart.

Living in our log hut was sheer comfort compared to the rigors of the march and the daily fear of death in combat. At first we merely relaxed and slept, then got out our sewing kits called "housewives" and our 'hole rank' was mended on our tattered uniforms. We have a saying that one hole in the seat of the britches indicates a captain, two holes a lieutenant and the seat of the pants all out indicates a private!

Several of our foragers smuggled a half gallon of "Ole Pop Skull" moonshine whiskey into camp in a frozen, hollowed-out watermelon, cached it beneath the floor of their hut, and tapped it with a long straw. When one of them wanted a drink he lay flat on the floor and sucked the straw. His comrades stood ready to cut him off after his Adam's apple registered his ration of two swallows!

The grey-backed fleas got so bad that one poem was the most popular in winter camp:

"Now I lay me down to sleep,
While grey-backs o'er my body creep;

TITHES OF BLOOD

If I should die before I wake,
I pray the Lord their jaws to 'Break'!

The rest of the time we all thought of home and wrote to our loved ones. I even started writing Little Liz Glover and bless Glory, she started writing me back!

A daily detail went every day to the slaughter pen for meat and most of the time the boys would bring back arms full of cow horns. We then spent many pleasurable hours scraping and drilling until we had some very respectable blowing horns. Before long, all of us had blowing horns and sometimes one company would bust loose blowing their horns, then another company would answer them and finally the whole regiment would follow suit. On one occasion our Col. P. F. Liddell sent word to the officer of the day to stop that horn blowing or he would put him under arrest. As fast as he would go from one company and quieten it down, another company would break loose blowing behind him. He did all he could but could not stop it. It was almost equal to the horn blowing around the walls of Jericho. For a long time after that, the 11th Mississippi went by the name of the horned regiment. We honestly believed that if we could ever have surrounded Washington City and blown our horns that it would immediately have fallen into our hands as Jericho did into the hand of Joshua!

As weeks lengthened into months, however, we grew tired of the inaction. The officers also became overbearing and irritable. We sometime played tenpins with 12-lb.

cannon balls which we rolled at the pins made of lengths of stove-wood. Sometime a few of the boys boxed for fun, sometime not for fun. Me and my brothers often went hunting for company food and sometime by mistake we brought back some not-so-wild turkeys, chickens and guineas from those un-cooperative plantations!

We even developed a spirit of friendliness with the blue-bellies over the river - especially during a memorable band concert by a top-notch Yankee band. The program began with a medley of Northern airs, patriotic tunes and war songs. This was well enough for listeners in blue, but not to the complete liking of our part of the audience stationed on the Southern bank.

"Now give us some of **our** songs!" we shouted from across the river.

Without hesitation the band swung into the tunes of "Dixie," "Maryland, My Maryland" and the "Bonnie Blue Flag." This brought forth a lusty and prolonged cheer from our whole division. Finally the music swelled into the tender strains of "Home, Sweet Home," and the countryside reverberated with the cheers of thousands of men on both sides of the stream. We then turned away back to our rude winter huts with tears in our eyes. We were a long way from Noxubee County, Mississippi.

The biggest form of recreation was snow ball fights. These events first started off as fights among squads, then companies and finally regiments and brigades, replete with officers in command and realistic military tactics being pursued. Our snow ball combat got so elaborate that Gen. A. P. Hill himself came over and joined the fray, not as the commander, but as one of the troops. That made us love him even more.

That particular fight got so wrought up that we had three bloody noses and two black eyes in our company alone!

While our men were recuperating from the "snow-ball wars", our company attended to the election of officers and other business. Our Captain, J. T. W. Hairston, and his brother, Samuel Hairston, transferred over to Gen. Jeb Stewart's cavalry and Sec. Lt. A. H. Ledbetter resigned. It was later reported that Captain Hairston was challenged to a duel by Lt. Col. Heros Von Borcke, Jeb's chief of staff. That probably scared him off his "high horse" a bit!

A terrible scourge of measles hit winter quarters and

Snowball fight in Confederate camp

WINTER QUARTERS

First Lt. W. H. Grey, Third Lt. Johnson, Privates W. Huckleby and T. H. Roberts died.

Isaac Albert, W. B. Cananah, J. E. Hairston, T. Hanes, A. J. Hinkle, Squeaky Sealy and Bill Autry were discharged. Rev. W. C. Hearn was elected Captain; W. H. Belton, 2nd Lieutenant; T. J. Mims, 3rd Lieutenant. Dr. W. B. Shields was appointed Assistant Surgeon. Dr. R. O. Davidson was also commissariat of the company and thus had leisure time to court the muses. He composed several stanzas of martial verse and then printed them. His most popular 'air' was dedicated to the Prairie Guards and was sung to the tune of *Dixie*:

> Oh, maple buds and dogwood blossoms
> Taters sweet and roasted 'possums
> Look away, look away, look away,
> > Dixie Land!

> Oh, topsy-turvy Yankeedom
> Where worthless arts and isms sprung
> Look away, look away, look away,
> > Dixie Land!

> We'll meet Ole Abe with armies brave,
> And whip the lying scoundrel knave,
> Look away, look away, look away
> > Dixie Land!

TITHES OF BLOOD

Our camp town ladies sho' are lookers,
We captured them from Ole Joe Hooker
Look away, look away, look away,
              Dixie Land!

McDowell crost that Rubicon—
His legions faltered, fled and run
Look away, look away, look away,
              Dixie Land!

If Yankees plead for terms and whiskey,
We'll give them hell to the tune of Dixie,
Look away, look away, look away,
              Dixie Land!

To popularize his productions, he organized a Glee Club
and we had several rehearsals. At the last one of his Club
singings we glided into the parody, which first made the
good old Presbyterian Dr. Shields laugh and then blush and
a little further on he dismantled the Club after giving it a
regulation cussing out!

At this camp, the new flag adopted by Congress was
received. Lieutenant Halbert's diary had this entry, Nov. 6,
1861. "The new Rebel battle flag was presented by the
Government and received at dress parade today by the 11th
Mississippi Regiment. Our boys were formed in hollow
square around it. With uncovered heads we held our
battered black hats over our hearts. Our captain, W. C.

WINTER QUARTERS

Hearn, led the prayer, 'In the name of our Lord Jesus, we ask the blessing of the God of Battles upon this sacred battle flag, that it might stand through all ages as the emblem of liberty, the hope of mankind and that as long as time may last, it may waive over a free and happy people." On it was inscribed 11th Mississippi Manassas.

While the Army was in winter quarters, the government asked the 12th month troops to re-enlist for two years and promised a $50.00 bounty and 60 day furlough to every man who would do so. The furlough was to be granted as the exigencies of the service would permit. On Feb. 8, 1862, the men of Company E, the Prairie Guards, who had re-enlisted drew lots for furloughs and 13 of the men started for home that evening. Most of us who drew blanks never received a furlough and others only at a late period of the war.

While we usually had a very good time at Camp Fisher, some days we would get trotted around the county, rather lively. General Whiting did not like to see us getting so fat and we afterwards heard that he started most of the false alarms and reported enemy advances just to get a chance to speed us to the potential danger spots. He did not know that he was shaking our soldiers' faith in official dispatches and that, later in the war, when the story of Jonah and the Whale was told by a visiting chaplain we regarded it as a mere camp rumor!

On the 9th of March, Johnston's army left the line of the Occaquan and retired south of the Rappahannock. We men of Whiting's brigade went to Fredericksburg, Virginia and here the men who were furloughed at Camp Fisher rejoined the command, bringing with them a good many recruits. They also brought about a dozen slaves to serve as cooks for the regiment and they were of great service in the camp and on the march. Some of them were captured while the army was in Pennsylvania, but they soon escaped and returned to their friends in the Confederate Army.

While we were at this place, Private Travis of our Company was discharged. Whiting's Division and Hampton's Legion were reviewed by Gen. Joseph E. Johnston.

Pvt. Leander Huckaby of Company E wrote that "most all of us caught the worst kind of a cold on the cars." Huckaby then came down with the measles. Illness did not dampen his appreciation of the Confederate capital, however.

Maj. Gen. W. H. C. Whiting

"I never seen a town 'till I saw Richmond," he wrote.

The 11th spent a quiet month in the defensive lines at Yorktown, and on April 21 the regiment selected new officers. Lt. Col. Phillip F. Liddell was elected colonel in place of William Moore, who had earlier resigned. There was a reorganization at a higher level as well. Despite his problem with liquor, Whiting was assigned command of a division which included his brigade, as well as the Texas Brigade under Brig. Gen. John B. Hood. Command of Whiting's Brigade went to Col. Evander M. Law of the 4th Alabama.

THE PENINSULA CAMPAIGN

Chapter V

Early in April, the division left on the dirt road leading to Richmond. All tents and extra clothing were shipped by rail. It was raining, sleeting and the roads were in a deplorable condition. The first night was especially hard on the new recruits. Some of them suffered terribly from this exposure.

The second evening we reached Milford, Virginia, and thence had transportation aboard railroad stock cars to Ashland. Remaining here a few days, we finally took the country roads down the peninsula to Yorktown on April 8th.

While at Yorktown, the company celebrated its First Anniversary and reorganized by electing H. P. Halbert, Captain; W. H. Belton, First Lieutenant; T. J. Mims, Second Lieutenant; Pleas Goolsby, Third Lieutenant. The regiment was organized and P. F. Liddell was elected Colonel, S. F. Butler, Lieutenant Colonel, and Sidney Evans, Major. Several of the recruits who had the measles were sent to Williamsburg, Virginia. One of them, Joseph C. Love, died.

On the 4th day of May, the Confederate high command ordered the evacuation of Yorktown. The next day Whiting's Division, composed of our own and Hood's Brigade, made a march of 35 miles to oppose Franklin's Corps which was sent to West Point for the purpose of cutting off Johnston's retreat. This force was driven back under cover of their gun boats at Barghamsville on the 7th by Hood's Brigade. After the Army had passed this threatening point, Whiting's division followed to the line of the Chickahominy.

May 30th was the date of the Battle of Seven Pines in which Company E actually engaged in combat for the first time. It was fought under many disadvantages on the Confederate side, but the final results were in our favor.

After several frontal attacks on Richmond, Union Gen. George McClellan made a daring naval troop movement down to the mouth of the James River at Yorktown. There he assembled his army and began his movement up the James and York River Peninsula toward Richmond.

We had to stop them. From May 6th to June 1st our various Confederate forces fought them tooth and toenail in a slow, carefully orchestrated retrograde movement. Old Joe Johnston, our beloved general, was famous for this. Actually he was outnumbered three to one but he was picking up reinforcements every day.

Six miles north of Williamsburg the entire army was falling back over a single road, and as there had been frequent rains, the road was badly cut up and the mud in many places was up to the axles of the guns. Finally a weak mule team balked with a gun, a 12-pounder Napoleon, in a deep hole. Every effort was made by the drivers to dislodge the gun, but without avail; and I found when our company got to the wheels, with as many men as could be utilized, that the horses could not be made to work in concert. The whole column to the rear was at a dead stand-still, when I observed a party of mounted officers coming down the road from the front, and in a few moments more I recognized Gen. Joseph Johnston at their head. We were all covered with mud and straining every muscle to extricate the gun, when the general, resplendent in full uniform, white gauntlets, and polished cavalry boots, rode up and halted by our side. We gave the military salute and stood like criminals awaiting sentence. To my surprise he remarked in a very kindly tone: "Well, boys, you seem to be in trouble." "Yes, sir, Lieutenant Goolsby replied; "and I am afraid we shall have to abandon this gun." "Oh, no, I reckon not! Let me see what I can do." Whereupon he leaped from his horse, waded out in the mire, seized one of the wheel-spokes, covered as it was with mud, and called out, "Now, boys, altogether!" The effect was magical, and the next moment the gun jumped clear of the mud-hole. After that our regiment used to swear by "Old Joe."

When the Confederate Army stopped for a breather at Seven Pines, the 11th Mississippi, still under General Whiting, arrived to join her brothers in the fray. As we marched up to the front line, we passed two strange looking twin two story farm houses side by side. Neither one had a gallery or even a door stoop. They looked like two large tombstones with seven scraggly looking pine trees standing out in the front yard. There had already been some skirmishing and artillery duels around this area and the place was all shot-up looking.

THE PENINSULA CAMPAIGN

Our company, E, was at the head of the column which arrived in the vicinity of Gen. Joe Johnston's headquarters at six A.M. There in front of us, we were totally blocked by troops of General Longstreet's division. That suited **us** just fine for we had rather **they** contact the enemy first anyway.

Lt. Gen. Joseph Eggleston Johnston

General Johnston then sent a message to Longstreet to get moving but Longstreet was not to be found. So we waited in the fog and rain and heat for three hours. The thought of impending death **did** cross our minds. This misery went on unabated all day long.

Finally, about 4:00 P.M. General Johnston got things sorted out and after making several counter marches, we were ready for a big push.

As we were formed up in columns to move out, General Whiting and Lt. Gen. Joseph Eggleston Johnston in all his glory joined us at the head of our column. General Johnston is a small man, but fine boned and elegant. His hands are delicate and they flutter like birds when he talks or gives commands.

Since we were still the point company, I could overhear some of what they were saying to each other. General Whiting did not want to move too far forward without support on his flanks. General Johnston replied, "Oh!

TITHES OF BLOOD

General Whiting, you are too cautious." Coming from General Johnston, that was a mouthful but it made me remember all those "cry wolf" games that General Whiting had made us play in winter camp!

At any rate, we were soon formed in line of battle in the edge of a copse of woods 400 yards in front of a Yankee battery of six Napoleon 12 Pounders, those damnable, human-killing shotguns, which we were certain were double loaded with canister shot.

Colonel Liddell had to reform us before advancing again into the cleared field. Half-flooded and studded with stumps, the open field was no better going than the woods. Our boys slipped and sloshed through "mud and water half a leg deep. Yankee cannon shot threw geysers of mud and water high in the air, drenching us and our ammunition. Crouching behind stumps, we struggled to clear our muskets and draw a bead on the distant Yanks.

After a brief reconnoiter, Gen. Dorsey Pender and General Whiting trooped our line and pointed to the guns with their swords. "Charge those guns!" Somebody screamed "Charge!" and we moved out in unison. The assault was fearsome and the Yanks definitely **were** firing cannister. We lost a good many boys but finally, with our color bearer down, Capt. P. F. Liddell screamed to me amid the cannon roar and whine of the canister shot; "Can you put our flag on those works?" "Yes, Suh!" I screamed and something down deep in me turned on. I picked up that tattered battle flag and, all of a sudden, I felt myself floating above my mess mates with the flag in some ancient and inexorable statement of defiance of death. The next thing I knew, I had waded a swamp and planted that flag on the Yankee breastworks. As I blinked through the battle smoke, I beheld an enlivening sight. All ten companies of our dear 11th Mississippi were right behind me and every powder stained mouth was agape with the high-pitched tremulous Rebel Yell which rent the air.

The Yankees broke and ran and we captured their breastworks and camp along with five cannon, clothing, provisions, medicine, small arms and, most important, 100 barrels of whiskey! As soon as we were relieved by a reserve regiment, I grabbed that precious flag and made my way back to our line.

As I came down off of that concussion plowed ridge my eyes again swept the hard earned ground we had wrested from the Yankees. To my horror I saw two lumps of bedraggled grey up on the ridge as still as stones. J. W. Beckham and Smith Lee would never sing "Dixie" again in the "Prairie Guards" glee club. Gone, too, were my close friends, Jehu Kirksey and W. S. Broadfoot, both wounded and captured by the Yankees. Our second lieutenant, T. J. Mims, was wounded along with J. T. Jones, J. G. Love, John Mims, Barney Quinn and J. Q. Mullins, who lost a leg. My friend Jere Gage of the University Greys was very lucky; he remained standing under fire while seventeen bullets tattered his uniform but his colorful captain of the "Greys", William Lowery, was seriously injured when a minie ball tore through his cheek and eye socket.

TITHES OF BLOOD

One of our old Noxubee/Lowndes County citizens, E. A. Erwin, was visiting the company and joined in the battle. During a lull in combat one of our orderlies returned from division headquarters with the awful news that Gen. Joseph E. Johnston had been seriously wounded and army command had passed to Gen. Gustavus Smith.

According to one Mississippian, Lt. Col. Samuel Butler tried to urge his soldiers on, "fishing the boys out from behind stumps with his crooked sabre, but to no avail. Before long the entire regiment had drifted back to its starting point as another unit launched a futile attack against Sumner's men.

The 11th Mississippi took 504 men into battle at Seven Pines and lost about 20 killed and 100 wounded, almost 24 percent of those engaged.

I had never conceived of such trials as we recently passed through. We were for days together without a morsel of food, excepting occasionally a meal of parched corn. . . . The army was kept on the march day and night and the roads were in some places waist deep in muck. . . . Many of the men became exhausted and some were actually stuck in the mud and had to be pulled out. . . . A more dejected looking bunch of troops, I never laid eyes upon. We were constantly plastered from head to toe with black, gumbo mud. . . . The men on the march ran through the gardens . . . devouring every particle of vegetables like the army worm leaving nothing at all standing. Whenever a cow or hog was found it was shot down and immediately devoured.

THE PENINSULA CAMPAIGN

Chickahominy Swamp

For us, the battle of Seven Pines was over. We were saddened by our losses but we had proved our valor and there were many toasts and much horn blowing that night!

Shortly thereafter, we were pulled out of the battle line and marched to a new flanking position. During this march, we saw a thrilling sight; our president, Jefferson Davis, and his entourage came riding toward our column. President Davis was well-mounted and his jutting chin looked even more pronounced by a goatee which made him look elegant but haughty. The man who rode beside him, however, was the most handsome specimen of Southern manhood I had ever seen with a clear, ruddy complexion set off by a neat white beard, deep intelligent brown eyes and a well-shaped Roman nose. He radiated a calm, commanding air but also had, at the same time, a certain kind of refined humility.

"Who is he?" someone whispered. "Gen. Robert E. Lee," Captain Butler replied, "and he was once offered command of the whole Yankee army." "I'm glad he's on our side, now," I thought. We soon learned that President Davis

Gen. Robert E. Lee

had given him command of **our** army which General Lee immediately named the Army of Northern Virginia.

Back at our rest area, someone asked General Whiting what he thought of the 11th Mississippi. "No more disorderly mob of men were got together to make an army," he replied, "and I cuss whenever I think of them, but, damn 'em, I wouldn't go into battle without 'em!"

Our regiment was also famous for its marksmanship. Most of us were country boys who had always hunted with a rifle, (with the exception of little Tommy McKie of the "University Greys"). Pore little Tommy was the regimental pet. We all treated him like our baby brother. Tommy wrote his mother back in Oxford every week, begging her to petition President Jefferson Davis to relieve him from duty as underage. His pardon from duty never came.

One day our corps commander, Gen. D. H. Hill, Ole Stonewall's brother-in-law, reported to our General Whiting the loss of a farmer's hog within our lines. He testified that a shot had been heard followed by a squeal. General Whiting replied soberly, "I am satisfied you are mistaken; when an 11th Mississippian shoots a hog, it **don't** squeal!

We enjoyed a well deserved rest after Seven Pines, washed off the smelly swamp mud and wrote and received letters from home. Some of our boys with minor wounds rejoined our unit.

Late on the evening of June 10, with our brigade still resting near the battlefield of Seven Pines, Colonel Law was summoned to the tent of General Whiting. Much to his

Gen. Daniel Harvey Hill

surprise, he learned that our brigade and Hood's were to be sent to reinforce Jackson in the Shenandoah Valley. The trip took nearly a week, and on June 16, Whiting joined forces with Jackson at Staunton.

The next morning, expecting to set out on one of Jackson's lightning marches, we new arrivals were astounded to learn that we had orders to start back in the direction we had just come. First by rail, then by foot, the 11th Mississippi, now part of Jackson's Army of the Valley, headed east toward Richmond. As each day passed it became more apparent that we, along with the rest of Jackson's army, were marching to reinforce Lee in front of Richmond. The movement to the Valley had been an elaborate ruse. We returned with Jackson to Ashville and on the 25th moved with him to flank the enemy's position at Mechanicsville, while troops from the Richmond line were also to attack. After a severe battle, the enemy retired to a stronger position on Beaver Dam Creek. Here A. P. Hill, D. H. Hill and General Longstreet assaulted the enemy's works until late in the night and renewed the attack on the 27th.

THE PENINSULA CAMPAIGN

When Jackson belatedly crossed the creek higher up, the enemy retreated to his strongly fortified position at Gaines Mill. The Battle of Gaines Mill was opened.

By 5 o'clock on the 27th of June the battle was in full progress all along the line. Longstreet's and our division commander, A. P. Hill's men were attacking in the most determined manner, but we were met by Yankee troops with courage as obstinate as our own. The Federals held doggedly to their works. After each bloody repulse we Confederates only waited long enough to re-form our shattered lines or to bring up support. Then we would again return to the assault. Besides the terrific fire in our front, a battery of heavy guns on the south side of the Chickahominy was in full play upon our right flank. There was no opportunity for maneuvering or flank attacks, as was the case with D. H. Hill on our extreme left. The enemy was directly in front, and he could only be reached in that direction. If he could not be driven out before night it would be equivalent to a Confederate disaster, and would involve the failure of General Lee's whole plan for the relief of Richmond. . . . It was a critical moment for us Confederates, as victory, which involved the relief or the loss of our capitol, hung wavering in the balance. Night seemed about to close the account against us, as the sun was now setting upon our gallant but so far fruitless efforts.

While matters were in this condition our division under General Whiting crossed with much difficulty the wooded and marshy ground below Gaine's Mill. We arrived in rear of that portion of the line held by the remnants of A. P. Hill's division. When we advanced to the attack a thin and irregular line of General Hill's troops were keeping up the fight, but, already badly cut up, could effect nothing, and were gradually wasting away under the heavy fire from the Federal lines. From the center of the division to the Chickahominy Swamp on the right the ground was open; on the left were thick woods. Our dear 11th Mississippi under the command of General Law advanced on the open ground while General Hood's command moved through the woods on our left.

As we moved forward to the firing we could see the other straggling Confederate line lying behind a gently rolling ridge that ran across the field parallel to the Federal position. We passed one Confederate battery in the edge of the field badly cut to pieces and silent. Indeed, there was no Confederate artillery then in action on that part of the field. The Federal batteries in front were in full play. The fringe of woods along the Federal line was shrouded in smoke and seemed fairly to vomit forth a leaden and iron hail.

Law's brigade advanced to the attack in two battle lines, the 11th Mississippi Regiment (Colonel Liddell) and the 4th Alabama (Lt. Colonel McLemore) forming the first line, and the 2nd Mississippi (Colonel Stone) and the 6th North Carolina (Colonel Avery) the second line. Hood had a similar formation on our left, but just as we came under fire, and before reaching the slope where the charge began, General Hood passed rapidly across our rear at the head of the 4th Texas regiment, closely followed by the 18th Georgia, also in his brigade. They came up on our right, extending our line in that direction. The 1st and 5th Texas regiments and the Hampton Legion of the same brigade remained on the left in the woods.

General Whiting rode along our line and ordered that there should be no halt when we reached the slight crest occupied by the few Confederate troops in our front, but that the charge should begin at that point in double-quick time, with trailed arms and without firing. Had these orders not been strictly obeyed the assault would have been a failure. No troops could have stood long under the withering storm of lead and iron that beat into our faces as we became fully exposed to view from the Federal lines. Passing over the scattered line of Confederates on the ridge in front, the whole division "broke into a trot" down the slope toward the Federal works. Men fell like leaves in an autumn wind as the Federal artillery tore gaps in our ranks at every step. The ground in rear of our advancing column was strewn thickly with the dead and wounded but not a gun was fired in reply. There was no confusion, and not a step faltered as our two grey lines swept silently and swiftly on. The pace became more rapid every moment. When our men were within thirty yards of the ravine, and could see the desperate nature of the work at hand, a wild Rebel Yell answered the roar of Federal musketry, and we rushed for the works. We Confederates were within ten paces of them when the Federals in the front line broke cover, and, leaving their log breastworks, swarmed up the hill in their rear, carrying away their second line with them in their rout. Then we had our "innings." As the blue mass surged up the hill in our front, our rifle fire was poured into it with terrible effect. The target was a large one, the range short, and scarcely a shot fired into that living mass could fail of its errand. The debt of blood contracted but a few moments before was paid, and with interest.

Firing as we advanced, we leaped into a ravine, climbed out on the other side, and over the lines of Union breastworks like water over a dam, reaching the crest of the hill beyond with such speed as to capture all fourteen pieces of the Federal artillery at that point. We had now reached the high plateau in rear of the center of Gen. Fitz John Porter's position, his line having been completely cut in two, and thus rendered no longer tenable. From the flanks of the great gap where Whiting's division had torn through, the Federal lines gave way in both directions.

Gen. James Longstreet

Gen. Richard H. Anderson's brigade, till then in reserve, passed through on the right, and led the way for Longstreet's division, while on the left the roll of musketry receded toward the Chickahominy, and we victorious Confederates screaming the Rebel Yell, announced that Jackson, Ewell, and D. H. Hill were sweeping that part of the field.

"The battle was won; the Federal infantry was in full flight toward the swamps of the Chickahominy and the bridges in their rear, leaving a large portion of their artillery in the hands of us Confederates. But the fighting was not all over. Several Federal batteries, posted in reserve on the further side of the plateau which the Confederates had gained, opened a rapid but rather ineffective fire, with the view of covering the retreat of their infantry.

Maj. Gen. E. M. Law

The 4th Texas and 18th Georgia regiments of Hood's, and our 11th Mississippi and the 4th Alabama of Law's brigade continued to advance across the plateau directly upon those batteries. And here occurred an incident of the battle which has been a subject of much acrimonious dispute among Federal officers, especially Generals Porter and Philip St. George Cooke, the latter commanding the cavalry on Porter's extreme left next to the Chickahominy.

TITHES OF BLOOD

In order to protect the guns upon which Law and Hood were advancing, General Cooke withdrew a portion of his command from the low grounds near the river and ordered a charge by a battalion of the 5th United States Cavalry upon the advancing Confederates. Our line was ragged and irregular, as every soldier knows will be the case after such fighting as it had passed through, and the opportunity seemed favorable to checking our further advance and saving the Yankee batteries from capture. The charge was directed upon the center of our Confederate battle line, which was halted and partly re-formed to receive it. Though delivered in a most gallant style, it was repulsed with heavy loss, including all but *one* of the officers who entered it. This episode consumed scarcely more time than it takes to write. In the meantime, those of the cavalry who escaped retreated through the artillery they were attempting to save, and in the confusion of the retreat, most of the guns were captured.

General Porter represented this charge as having been made on his extreme left (Longstreet's right), and beyond the stream along which his infantry line was originally formed, and severely censured General Cooke, charging him with throwing the artillery into confusion by retreating through it and preventing it from checking the Confederate advance. His statement as to the locality of his cavalry attack and his charges against General Cooke cannot be reconciled; for, had Cooke's cavalry attacked where General Porter says it did it would have been utterly impossible for its line of retreat to have passed anywhere near the position of the

61

batteries, and its flight after the repulse could have had no effect whatever upon the loss of the guns. Hood's and Law's line of advance was directly across the plateau from the left center of Porter's original line, where they had broken it, passing south of and near the Watts house on the plateau; and as the cavalry charge was made upon *them*, and *they* captured the guns, it follows that the charge could only have been made *there*, and not half a mile nearer the Chickahominy, where it would have been objectless, and indeed ridiculous.

I speak positively on this point, as I was an eye-witness of the whole affair, having been one of the troops who received the cavalry charge, and was engaged in the capture of the guns. Whatever may be said to the contrary, it is certain that the batteries, having no infantry supports, did not check our advance for a moment. The diversion by the cavalry, on the other hand, did delay their capture for the short period it took to repulse it, and gave time for the artillerists to save some of their guns.

While these events were taking place on the plateau, heavy firing was going on immediately upon the left of the gap in the Federal line through which we had passed, now some distance in our rear. As the front was clear, the 11th Mississippi was halted and re-formed. This had scarcely been done when a Confederate cheer rose from the woods in the direction of the firing, and a large body of Federals rushed out upon the plateau on our left and rear, retreating rapidly and in great confusion. Part of them passed to our left, while the greater portion were running across our rear in the attempt to escape to the Chickahominy Swamp in that direction. Our rear rank was faced about, and they were called on to surrender. No attention was paid to the first summons, and a few shots were fired into our ranks. A volley from our rear rank, which now faced them, induced them to listen to reason, and they at once threw down their arms in token of surrender. The 1st and 5th Texas regiments and the Hampton Legion (Hood's brigade), which it will be remembered were on the left of Law's brigade in the original line of attack, had not driven the Federal line in their front at the same time with the rest of the division; but they had now broken it, and were closely following the fugitives. The prisoners, about 800 in number, were turned over to the 5th Texas regiment, which was close on the Yankees' heels.

The works were carried and the guns were captured. An effort was made by the Yankees to recapture the guns by calvary charge, but it was a disastrous failure.

We front-line boys also noted that the Rebel Yell varied in pitch with the viciousness of the attack or the state of origin of the troops. Our Mississippi Rebel Yell was a very high pitched blood curdling scream.

The Company lost some fine men in this battle. J. E. Halbert and William Norwood, my cousin, were killed. Wounded and discharged were: J. W. Carr, H. P. Halbert, Captain Thomas Carr, F. H. Ervin, John Jones, J. C. Love and Sol Steverson.

On the evening of the 28th, President Davis, acting almost like one of the troops, visited the quarters of the 11th

Mississippi and made a very complimentary speech to the Brigade. That same day Socrates Curtin of Company E died in agony with typhoid fever.

Our forces under Gen. Stonewall Jackson crossed the Grapevine Bridge and on the evening of the 30th overtook the enemy at White Oak Swamp. Here we were exposed to heavy fire from Union artillery. The stream was crossed early the next morning and the Yankees were pursued down the Wills Church Road. We passed over the Frayser Farm where the battle was fought the previous day. A little further down the road, the 11th Mississippi saw Gen. Robert E. Lee once again. We were very much pleased with his bearing and we gave him a huge cheer.

About 3 miles from here we were marching rapidly. Everyone was in fine spirits with the 11th Mississippi at the head of the column when suddenly the enemy's shells began

Charge of Confederates upon Randol's Battery at Frayser's Farm

busting over our heads. We had overtaken the Yankees at Malvern Hill where they proposed to fight. The greater part of the day was spent in getting the different commands up and into position. Whiting's Division occupied the left and we suffered very little in the battle. B. B. Tomlinson of our company was wounded.

During the night the enemy retreated and was found the next day under cover of his gunboats at Harrison Landing. The Division remained at the front for a few days and then moved back to Richmond. While here, General Whiting was promoted; in fact, he was kicked upstairs and was assigned to a command in North Carolina, which was like being banned to Dry Tortuga.

General Hood was put in command of our division. General Hood was an outstanding commander. We were extremely happy with this turn of events. Col. E. M. Law of the Fourth Alabama, also a wonderful officer, commanded our brigade.

Three men of Company E were discharged July 27th: Barney Quinn, Saul Stephenson, being over conscript age, and James Jones, being under age. My cousin, John Norwood, of our company died about this time with a possible ruptured appendix.

Following the Battle of Malvern Hill, Hood's Division enjoyed several weeks in the vicinity of Richmond.

The morning of August 30 came quietly. While Lee waited for Pope to renew his attacks, the befuddled Union general spent the morning arguing with his subordinates, refusing to believe that the Confederates were not fleeing. The silence was finally broken shortly after 3:00 p.m. when Brig. Gen. Fitz John Porter's V Corps launched a final attack on Jackson's position. Two companies of the 11th were posted as skirmishers near Groveton a half mile in front of

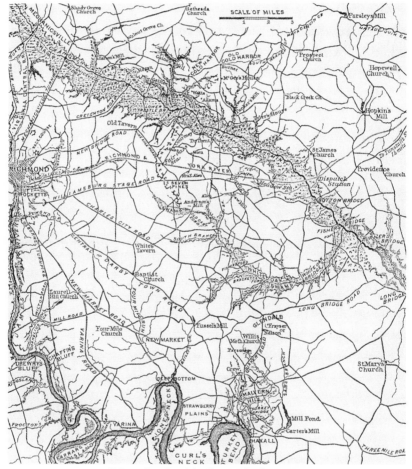

7-Days Battle of the Peninsula Campaign

Law. The Yankees fought back stubbornly-the colonel of the 12th Massachusetts fell just in front of the Chickasaw Guards-but were soon forced back to Henry House Hill. As one member of the Prairie Guards wrote, "It was a hard battle but the Yankees run at last and we left them lying thick on the ground."

The battle finally ended for the men of the 11th Mississippi around 6:00 p.m. They had lost touch with their own brigade, and the troops they were with were too disorganized to pursue Pope's beaten army. Lost but victorious, the 11th spent the night on the battlefield. Like Whiting before him, Law praised Colonel Liddell for his "consummate ability," and reported that our regiment had suffered a loss of nine killed and 69 wounded.

SECOND MANASSAS
Chapter VI

About the middle of August the 11th Mississippi, still in Hood's division, left Richmond for the new Theater of War in Culpepper, Virginia. The summer heat was intense and our troops marched by night and rested during the day. Our movements were directed by General Longstreet, to whose command the division was attached. When Longstreet reinforced Jackson, the Yankee General Pope skedaddled beyond the Rappahannock.

On the 25th Jackson left the main army by a circuitous route from Manassas. Longstreet continued the artillery duels at the various fords until daylight of the 27th when he crossed at Warrentown Springs and pushed on through Thoroughfare Gap where the enemy disputed his passage. In this battle, Hood's Division was sent over the mountain to flank the position and we did not become engaged.

Early on the 29th, Longstreet's forces pursued

Gen. John Bell Hood

the enemy through Gainesville and we came upon the field of Manassas about noon. We shook out skirmishers to probe the Yankee position and promptly got into a fierce fire fight with the Yankee skirmishers. In this first day of the battle of Second Manassas, P. W. Nash lost a leg and M. M. Williams was wounded.

The next day our company was again thrown forward as skirmishers and after firing all of our cartridges we fell back before a line of Yankee infantry. In this skirmish, D. S. Martin lost an arm, P. J. Brown and Houston Quinn were wounded and discharged and J. L. Sherman, L. Huccaby were severely wounded. I received a flesh wound in my left thigh but continued to fight.

After being supplied with ammunition, our company again moved forward, this time on the right of the turnpike where it was protected somewhat by the timber. From our position on the skirmish line, we saw a picture that cannot be painted or described. It was Stonewall Jackson's men standing at bay, while General Pope hurled his solid blue masses against them. Rebel and Yankee firing ceased on our part of the line and the men on both sides gathered in groups to gaze upon the scene. After a long while, the old Rebel Yell was heard above all other sounds of the conflict and the battle flag of the Confederacy darted forward in one of those charges so enlivening to us, and so terrifying to the enemy. Longstreet's forces now drove the Yankees from the field and as a regiment swept by, four men of our company got excited and joined it, one of whom, John Grizzle, was killed.

TITHES OF BLOOD

Longstreet's troops rested on the battlefield until the night of the 31st and then followed Stonewall Jackson, who was trying to intercept Pope's retreat. When Pope's army escaped to the fortifications around Washington, our army turned toward Leesburg and crossed the Potomac into Maryland. We occupied Frederick City for a few days. Hood's division then went to Hagerstown and on September 15th we were sent back to support D. H. Hill in the Battle of Boonesborough Gap. The 11th Mississippi had 9 killed and 69 wounded in this battle.

Sharpsburg

CHAPTER VII

During the night of September 16th the Division came down from Boonesboro Gap and the next morning crossed a meandering water course called Antietam Creek and took possession of the Town of Sharpsburg.

As our weary, footsore columns climbed a gradual slope from the creek, Gen. Robert E. Lee gestured to an undulating ridge on which stood the Dunker Church, "We will make our stand on those hills," he ordered. Late in the day, Hoke's Brigade became engaged and Gen. Evander Law's Division

Jackson's men wading Antietam Creek

composed of the 11th Mississippi, 2nd Mississippi, 4th Alabama and the 6th North Carolina made up the second line in support.

Our regiment was then exposed to a heavy enfilading artillery fire, which made some of the boys pray out loud. We called the 12-lb. parrot shells "lamp posts" and the 12-lb. case shot shells "wash kettles". These shells were the usual cause of a fairly common malady called "buck ague" which causes men to shiver from a cause other than cold weather. When troops are caught out in the open like this everyone hugs the ground as if they loved it. Line and field officers are no exception and regardless of rank they also lay

ramrod hoecakes

TITHES OF BLOOD

Confederate dead at the Dunker Church

beneath the infernal canopy of hissing lead and screaming iron like the rest of us.

As darkness fell, our men lay helpless in the woods, facing north, while the heavy guns enfiladed our position from the east. We Mississippians could see the glowing fuses flicker as the shells passed above the trees, hear the cracking of limbs which marked the passage of the shells through the foliage, and feel the explosions which showered us with leaves and iron splinters. A shell or shot passing along the line could have massacred an entire company, but the deadly missiles fell just to the front or the rear of our position. Tragically, twenty paces to the front of the 11th was our commanding officer, Col. Phillip Liddell. In the darkness a shell burst overhead, sending a fragment into our colonel's torso. The wound proved mortal, and Col. Liddell lingered painfully for two days before dying. General Longstreet eulogized Liddell as "an officer of great merit, modesty, and promise." After the battle, our men of Hood's division bivouacked in the woods near the old Dunker Church on Hagerstown Road. At daylight on the 17th of September, the woods were shelled and at sunrise we moved forward to meet the advance of the enemy.

Our overall commander was Gen. John Bell Hood, born in Kentucky but now a Texan. He was thirty-one years old and six feet tall with a tawny red beard and a huge, sad face. He deeply believed in our cause and the St. Andrew's Cross.

After our bloody fight yesterday, we were held back behind the main battle line in reserve. At daylight we arose hungry and set about to rustle up some victuals for breakfast.

The commissary wagons finally showed up late per usual and they only brought flour.

When the emergency bugle call to arms sounded, we were baking hoecakes on our Enfield ramrods. We quickly bolted down the half baked dough and fell into line, still hungry and fighting mad at having our breakfast so rudely interrupted.

At 7:00 A.M. our division, 2,300 strong, came pouring out of the woods, crossed the turnpike at the gap in the fence near the Dunker Church and pushed on into the pasture south of the corn field.

Then we men of Law's Brigade: the 11th Mississippi, 2nd Mississippi, 4th Alabama and 6th North Carolina, deployed in skirmish order in the fields immediately north of Samuel Poffenberger's farm, adjacent to the old Dunker Church.

The battle flags of the 11th and 2nd Mississippi proudly bore the battle honors Manassas, Seven Pines, Gaines Mill and Second Manassas.

Then at the command of Major General Hood, our brigade and Wofford's brigade which made up his division, charged down the hill and pressed for the cornfield and bodily knocked Starke's and Taliaferro's badly mauled Union

Rallying behind the turnpike fence

troops out the other side. The soul chilling Rebel Yell echoed across the corn field and still our wild men continued to charge the Yankees across the bloodied ground between the corn field and the Smoketown road.

We paused only long enough to let some wounded boys back through our ranks. Then we raised the Rebel Yell and fired a volley that was like a scythe mowing down the Yankees as well as the corn stalks.

Our Gallant Hood then ordered a general advance all along our line. We again charged through the bloody wreckage of the dead and wounded from earlier fighting. They lay so thick that we had to watch our every step so as not to step on them.

In a few minutes we had pushed all the way through the corn field to the rail fence at its north boundary and sent a volley into the flank of one of "Old Snapping Turtle" George Mead's brigades. The blue-bellies broke and ran. We heard one of their officers shout "Rally, boys, rally! Die like men;

don't run like dogs!" One of the Yanks hollered back, "Live dog beats a dead man!"

The fury of battle was upon us, we all leaped the rail fence and ran into the open field beyond then blazed away at the Pennsylvanians to our left and right and at the batteries on their front that were firing double-shotted canister at a range less than 200 yards. Their unprotected artillery did not last long against our infantry fire at that short distance. The gunners were dropping like flies and we killed their battery horses, too.

We silenced two of their cannons and the reserve battery took off before it could unlimber and open fire.

We halted for a well-earned breather and checked our ammo. We were almost out. It was 8:00 A.M. when a sudden and unexpected silence fell over the battlefield, broken only by the occasional crack of a rifle or the clang of a cannon shot. We still heard the moans and screams of thousands of wounded men. My friend Capt. W. W. Scales was wounded way out in front of our line. A kind-hearted Yankee colonel named Norman J. Hall of the 7th Michigan stopped to patch him up and give him water. "You fought and stood well," Colonel Hall told him. "Yes," old Scales replied, "and here I lie!"

As the day wore on I was increasingly conscious of exhaustion. Though accustomed before the war to long hours of labor on the farm or extended jaunts in pursuit of game, I found combat the hardest work I had ever done. My fatigue was sharpened by the fact that rest and food had been

TITHES OF BLOOD

Confederate dead along the corn field fence

The charge across the Burnside Bridge

scarce during the days before the battle. By mid-afternoon my strength was so depleted that I could hardly load and fire my gun.

Right behind our line, General Evans of South Carolina rode up to our General Hood. "Where is your division?" General Evans asked. "Dead on the field!" replied General Hood.

Mercifully, we were soon ordered back to a consolidation position near the corpse-strewn yard of the Dunker Church, where we agonized over the final outcome of the battle. Since we were at an elevation, we could see the slaughter along the sunken road that went on unabated for hours.

While we were enjoying this ringside seat to Confederate victory, an unfortunate event occurred. I was suddenly knocked off my feet when a partially spent Yankee bullet struck my right leg, knocking a chunk out of my shin bone and giving my leg a slight fracture. The pain was awful but luckily we were right near the field hospital.

Dr. Holt cauterized the wound, splinted and bandaged it and gave me a healthy swig of laudanum. This killed the pain in short order and I was soon back out on crutches with my messmates enjoying the bloody spectacle below. Finally, with no objective gained, save to murder each other, that engagement petered out.

Another Federal regiment soon appeared on the crest before the now-bloody cornfield. Because the Yankees were on higher ground, the majority of their fire-like that of their predecessors-flew harmlessly over our heads. Our fire, however, was quite effective. We had nearly silenced the opposing troops when, much to our surprise, our men in the 11th were ordered to retreat. The large gap between the 4th Alabama in the East Woods and the rest of the brigade in the cornfield had been penetrated by Union regiments, whose presence threatened the right-rear of Law's line.

As they retired through the field, Lt. Colonel Butler fell mortally wounded as the shell and shot which had formerly been passing overhead now fell amongst us. With the loss of Butler, the senior surviving officer on the field was Maj. T. S. Evans. The ill-luck that had thus far plagued our field officers at Sharpsburg continued unabated. Evans, who probably never learned that command of the regiment had devolved onto his shoulders, was killed outright by enemy fire shortly after Butler fell. When we who survived assembled south of the cornfield, we discovered to our dismay that our colors were missing. Color bearer William Kidd had died on the field, and our flag had fallen to the ground with him.

It was still morning when Hood's Division retired behind the Dunker Church and out of immediate danger. Fresh Confederate troops drove the advancing Federals out of the cornfield once more, but our flag could not be found; the retreating Yankees had taken the prize with them.

About then, however, another Yankee Corps under General Ambrose Burnside came on the field just south of a stone bridge that spanned Antietam Creek. This new set of Yankee troops then set about trying to cross that little stone bridge as if it were the pivot point of civilization. We watched as wave after wave of Yankees were beaten back by our boys under the command of the old Southern politician and firebrand, Robert Toombs of Georgia. My messmate Barney Quinn who was water bearer because of a previous wound pointed down there toward the tortured bridge. "Tom, I went down there for water yesterday and that creek's so shallow you can wade it most anywhere! Those Yankees could have splashed across that creek anywhere they wanted to."

That pretty well summed up Ole Burnside, all fluff and sideburns but no common sense!

Something happened about then that was greatly enlivening to our spirits. Burnside's troops finally succeeded in taking the bridge after he had promised them all a bunch of whiskey. The Yankees then surged up the hill and we could see that our whole army was in danger due to this unexpected flanking maneuver.

Just in the nick of time, Gen. A. P. Hill, picturesque in his red battle shirt, with three of his brigades of 2,500 men who had force-marched seventeen miles that day from Harpers Ferry and had waded the Potomac, arrived on the battle field directly on Burnside's flank. Tired and footsore, those boys forgot their woes in that supreme moment and with no time for water or rest they pitched into a full flank attack. The blue line staggered, hesitated and A. P. Hill pressed home the attack! Our red battle flags danced like birds of war over the high-pitched, bone-chilling screams of the Rebel Yell! The blue line collapsed and skedaddled back across Antietam

Gen. Ambrose Powell Hill

Bridge. Again A. P. Hill, as at Manassas, Harpers Ferry and elsewhere, had struck with the hand of Mars. No wonder that both Lee and Jackson in their dying words called on A. P. Hill for succor. The Battle of Sharpsburg, which the Yankees named Antietam, was over.

This battle has been described as one of the most stubborn of the war there in the corn field. Since a large detachment of Lee's army was absent at Harper's Ferry, we were fearfully outnumbered.

The 11th Mississippi lost our gallant Col. P. F. Liddell,

Rations from the stalk

Lt. Col. S. F. Butler, Maj. Sidney Evans, and several company commanders. Our brave color bearer, Thomas Kidd, was killed and our flag was lost. In our company there was killed: John Donly, Joseph Howarth; wounded was Capt. J. P. Halbert and Capt. W. W. Scales. J. L. Edmonds was given a furlough to carry home the remains of his brother, Captain Nevil Edmonds, who was killed in the corn field charge. Our total loss was 8 killed and 96 wounded.

Our army is almost starved out. Our rations have been beef and flour since we left Richmond and not more than half enough per man. Many times we had green corn and apples issued to us and were glad to get that.

After the Battle of Sharpsburg, where all of the regimental officers were lost, there was a dispute among the captains of the individual companies of the 11th Mississippi as to who would command the regiment. Twenty-year-old Capt. William Benjamin Lowry of Company A, the University Greys, claimed the position on the basis that he was the senior captain and Capt. Francis M. Green of Company G, the Lamar Rifles, on the basis that his company was the first reorganized after the re-enlistments in early 1862. (It should be noted that both companies were organized at Oxford, Mississippi in Lafayatte County). On the 25th of September 1862, Captain F. M. Green was promoted to Colonel and W. B. Lowry to Lieutenant Colonel. After Lt. Colonel Lowry returned to his home for surgery to correct an eye injury incurred during the Battle of Seven Pines, he wrote several letters to the Confederate Congress pleading his case that the colonelcy of the Eleventh belonged to him. Initially, the congress ruled that he was senior to Green and should have received the position but President Jefferson Davis reversed the decision on a technicality and let Green's promotion stand. When Lowry returned in early 1863, Colonel Green notified Lowry of the action of the President and that he was in command of the 11th Mississippi, whereby Lowry answered, "It makes not a bit of difference what you are. I will command this regiment." The two colonels then exchanged sharp words with each other and a challenge was issued from Lowry to Green. Captain Jonathan R. Prince,

SHARPSBURG

Company D, the Neshoba Rifles, was the bearer of that challenge. Colonel Green had both of them arrested. Prince was later freed and rejoined his company but Lowry spent most of his time furloughed for continued medical problems from the Seven Pines wound, eventually retiring the 1st of December 1864.

Colonel Francis M. Green thus inherited one of the most colorful of the Mississippi regiments, one which proudly claimed a mixed reputation; it was widely known as an unruly regiment, hopelessly immune to discipline but always ready for a fight. The regiment was also noted for its conspicuous gallantry and reckless abandon on the field of battle.

On the night of the 18th, Lee's army forded the Potomac near Shepherdstown. Hood's division soon after went into camp at the big spring not far north of Winchester. There was read here at dress parade, a general order from headquarters from Gen. Robert E. Lee highly complementing our division for gallantry on the field of Sharpsburg. The Yankees got medals for bravery but we all had much rather have Marse Roberts' approval. The command camped here until the last days of October and then moved to the neighborhood of Culpepper Courthouse.

A few weeks later the 2nd and 11th Mississippi were sent to Richmond and reunited with the 42nd Mississippi Regiment and the 26th Mississippi Regiment and these formed Brig. Gen. Joseph R. Davis' Mississippi Brigade. The 54th North Carolina Regiment was shortly added to it.

On November 8, 1862, Special Order 236 directed that

the 2nd and 11th Mississippi Infantry Regiments be detached
from the Army of Northern Virginia and report to Richmond.
In the Confederate capital, the regiments were joined by the
42nd Mississippi and the 55th North Carolina to form a new
brigade under the command of Brig. Gen. Joseph R. Davis,
the president's nephew.

Tarheel Peace Keeping
Chapter VIII

From Richmond our brigade was sent to Goldsbourgh, North Carolina to oppose a force under the Yankee General Foster who was supposedly advancing on the town. The 11th Mississippi arrived while a warm battle was raging a few miles distant across the river. Foster, learning that reinforcements were arriving, retreated rapidly and we did not become engaged.

We soon went into camp about a mile east of town and we began to study and soon learned the Tarheel vernacular. Our stay at this place was quite pleasant for we had all saved their homes from destruction and the local lovelies were very appreciative of that fact. They had met us at the depot with many expressions of joy and when we were called back to Virginia they could not conceal their sadness. As the railway cars bore us out of the depot, the last expressions heard were "you'unses come back when you kin';" but the vicissitudes of war prevented our return. About the time of our final winding up in 1862, a few men of the brigade who had been home on furlough and were returning to Virginia were stopped at Salisburg, North Carolina, and under Colonel J. N. Stone of the 2nd Mississippi tried to hold the town against a portion of Sherman's forces. Here H. C. Halburt and John K. Woods were captured. From Goldsbourgh, the brigade was sent by rail to Blackwater Bridge, Virginia. On arrival the brigade went into camp near Franklin and remained there until April 11, 1863.

Here Thomas Copeland of our company was killed by a Yankee captain of calvary in a personal encounter. At this line, we had no battle of importance, only a few skirmishes, but pickett duty was rather heavy. A large party of scouts was detailed to patrol the country between the Blackwater and Suffolk Rivers.

One day while we were on picket duty along the river, Leander Huckaby called out "Yank!" and receiving a prompt answer, requested to the enemy that there be no firing on the pickett line during the day. My friend, Jere Gage of Company A, proposed to exchange newspapers, holding one up in his hands. Mr. Yank said all right and started toward our line with one in his hand. Jere went to meet him, then another of our boys and then another, and so on until our whole picket force had left our rifle pits. The river was halfway between us and when we got down to the river bank a Yank was already in a skiff on our side and he offered to put us across. We accepted his invitation and shortly our whole picket force was over in Yankee territory.

By this time a big crowd of Yanks were around us, some proposing to make peace, some swapping buttons and other things; and the proposition was made to some of the boys to go up town and have a game of poker. We were having a big time until a Yankee officer came rushing down, very much excited, and yelled out, "What does all this mean?" He said the like was never heard of; and if the crowd did not disperse immediately, the batteries would be opened on it. He refused to allow the skiff to cross the river, and I thought we were in trouble for sure; but another officer standing near us remarked, "Boys, don't pay any attention to that damn fool. They know better than to fire into their own men. We will see that none of you are harmed and are put back safe on your side of the river." I was convinced that day that were it not for officers and politicians, we enlisted men could end the war immediately.

So we all shook hands, with a good-bye and good luck, and were put safely across. Not a gun was fired during the whole day. We went back into our rifle pits, and after dark we were called in and marched the whole night, evacuating the area.

In the spring we were reinforced and our unit was advanced on Suffolk, Virginia, which we besieged for a few weeks, but no general battle was brought on. The place was well fortified and had a strong garrison, together with gun boats in the river. In one of the almost daily skirmishes on the picket line, Samuel Stephenson, of the Prairie Guards was wounded.

After the army supplies from that section had been secured, which seemed to have been the only object of the campaign, our troops were withdrawn to our old line on the Blackwater River where we then spent a few weeks fishing and foraging.

While we were here, a new novel hit the literary world like a bombshell. Several of the "Greys" received copies from home. The book was *Les Miserables* by some Frenchman named Victor Hugo. Most of our boys couldn't or wouldn't read this panty-waist mish-mash but one good thing did come of the book. Instead of Les Miserables, we named ourselves Lee's Miserables!

While there we did monotonous picket duty while quartered in a huge warehouse down by the Rappahannock. On the last night that we were there, we set up another theatrical production for amusement and, as always, the star performer was my friend Jere Gage of the University Greys. Jere had a striking stage presence with his handsome well-modeled profile with a tousled shock of reddish-blonde hair, deep blue eyes, the muscles of a born athlete and a deep refined Southern accent. Jere had majored in English at the University of Mississippi before going into law so he genuinely loved poetry and elocution.

Jere mounted the makeshift stage with a flourish amid the guttering candles placed there for maximum dramatic effect by little Tommy McKie, our stage manager. Jere announced that he would give a paraphrased reading from the book, *Lays of the Scottish Chiefs* by William Edmonstone Aytoun. Before he could begin, Leander Huckaby blurted out that that was not exactly the kind of "lay" that he needed! After the roar of laughter had settled down, Jere began the reading in his molasses rich voice.

TITHES OF BLOOD

"Sound the fife and cry the slogan-
      Let Rebel Yells soon shake the air
With its wild triumphal music,
      Worthy of the freight we bear.

Let the hills of Mississippi
      Hear once more our Battle song,
Swell within their glens and valleys,
      As we Rebels march along.

      Never from a field of combat
      Never to a deadlier fray,
Was more nobler symbols carried,
      Than our Battle Flags today.

Never since the valiant Stonewall,
      On Virginia's bosom bore
Chancellorsville, his greatest victory
      Though he's on the yonder shore.

Lo, he is our greatest martyr,
      Lo, we bring the conquering Grame
Crowned as best beseems a victor,
      From the altar of his fame;

TARHEEL PEACEKEEPING

Fresh and bleeding from the battle
    Whence his spirit took its flight,
Midst the crashing of the armies
    And the thunder of the fight.

Strike, I say, in notes of vengeance,
    As we march o'er moor and lea,
Brothers, gird yourselves for battle
    Under our dear Robert Lee.

See! His valiant blood is mingled
    With our battle flag's red fold,
See how calm he looks and stately
    Like the Christian Knights of old.

See, once more, my gallant comrades,
    His pure gaze - the falcon's eye,
Redden with its inner lightening
    As the hour of fight draws nigh.

Then we'll hear that noble voice,
    Clearer than a trumpet's call,
Bid us fight for love of country,
    Bid us win the field, or fall!

TITHES OF BLOOD

On the heights above Antietam
    Yester-morn our army lay;
Slowly rose the mist in columns
    From the river's broken way;

Hoarsely roared the swollen torrent
    With its stone bridge wrapt in gloom,
When we Rebels rose together
    From our lair amidst the broom.

Then we fixed our bayonets
    As our Enfields down we drew
Checked our sixty rounds of bullets
    As we proved them to be true.

And we prayed the prayer of soldiers
    And we cried the gathering cry,
And we clasped the hands of kinsmen
    And we swore to do or die.

General Lee then rode before us
    On Traveler, his steed of might,
Well the cowering Yankee soldiers
    Knew that charger in a fight.

But he raised his hand for silence,
    "Soldiers! I have sworn a vow,
Ere the evening star shall glisten
    On the Southland's lofty brow,

TARHEEL PEACEKEEPING

By its sacred land I charge ye,
  By its ruined hearth and shrine-
By the blighted hopes of Dixie
  By your injuries and mine-

Strike this day as if the anvil
  Lays beneath your blows the while,
The timid army of McClellan
  Trembles like a frightened child

Strike! and drive the trembling Yankee,
  Backward o'er the stormy froth.
Let them tell their pale convention
  How we fared within the North.

Let them tell that Southern Honor
  Is not to be bought nor sold.
As we scorn our foeman's anger
  As we loathe his foreign gold.

Strike! and when the fight is over,
  If ye look in vain for me,
Where the dead are lying thickest,
  Search for Robert Edward Lee!"

Then Jere boomed, "To the Southern Confederacy and to
victory!" The whole place erupted into a giant and continuous
Rebel Yell!

The flickering candlelight played across the gaunt, hollow-

96

eyed faces of these brave but vulnerable young men. Even through their momentary joy loomed the indescribable pathos of the doomed. This, then, was a blood brotherhood, born in this cauldron of deprivation, danger and death. They were no longer fighting for or against some abstract ideal espoused by idealistic politicians on either side, they, like the Spartans at Thermapole, were now fighting for each other.

Gettysburg
Chapter IX

From the main Confederate line at Suffolk, our Brigade was sent to Fredericksburg and placed in Maj. Gen. Henry Heth's Division of A. P. Hill's Corps.

We started on the Pennsylvania campaign about the first of June. The dust, which once puffed and puddled under a single foot-fall, now billowed up in buff, choking clouds which strangled and blinded our marching column.

The long hot march to Gettysburg was awful but it was a real hardship on our regimental favorite, Sergeant Jere Gage of Company A. Jere was seriously wounded in the hip at the Battle of Gaines' Mill and he was still in great pain and limped badly. He grimly joked that he only had a "little hitch in his git-a-long". A lot of soldiers would have opted for the muster-out role but not Jere who struggled along trying vainly to keep up with his messmates because he couldn't imagine them going into combat without him.

Everyone was miserable and tempers flared. When Captain Lowry placed several of our boys under arrest when they broke ranks to get water every enlisted man began calling him **Corporal** Lowry. That tactic eventually worked because he soon dropped charges against those poor boys who had been about to die of thirst.

On June 30, 1863, Brig. James Johnston Pettigrew and his first brigade of Heth's division advanced southeastward from Cashtown, Pennsylvania toward Gettysburg. They soon discovered Union troops near Gettysburg and withdrew, obeying General Lee's order to probe the enemy, but not to bring on a full scale engagement. The next day, July 1st, the 11th Mississippi was ordered to guard Heth's division's wagon trains arrayed around Cashtown. We boys of the "Prairie Guards" were mighty happy for the rest after the fearful march to Pennsylvania. The rest of our brigade under General Davis was ordered to advance once more down the Cashtown road and (hopefully) on into Gettysburg, ostensibly to procure shoes.

At Marsh Creek, three miles from Gettysburg, they encountered two brigades of Union cavalry commanded by Brig. Gen. John Buford. Skirmishers were thrown forward and the Battle of Gettysburg began. Buford's force was armed with breech loading Sharps carbines which had a rapid rate of fire. This greatly slowed our advance, giving Buford time to call up much needed support, which soon arrived in the form of Maj. Gen. John Reynolds and his I Corps. As General Reynolds was deploying his troops, he was shot dead by one of our boys down by Marsh Creek.

Both sides then deployed on a broad front on either side of the Cashtown road and the battle rapidly escalated. Various brigade and division actions erupted all over the area behind the Lutheran Theological Seminary. Brig. Gen. Lysander Cutler's brigade which contained the equally famous "Irish Brigade" and "The Black Hats" soon relieved General Buford's cavalrymen.

TITHES OF BLOOD

When the Yankees topped the ridge with their bagpipe band playing "Here Come the Campbells", one of our skirmishers screamed back, "It ain't the militia, it's them damn 'black hats'!" Responding to the challenge, the 11th Mississippi charged them with a resounding Rebel Yell and the vaunted Union line gave way. We drove them back toward Gettysburg, killing and wounding many and capturing two beautiful silk battle flags.

Then the tide of battle turned and our boys were flanked and driven back into a deep railroad cut where a fierce battle raged and we lost many officers and men. Brig. Gen. James Jay Archer and most of his Tennessee brigade were captured. Gen. A. P. Hill, our corps commander, sent in several more reserve divisions which not only saved many of our boys locked in combat, but the fresh Confederate troops finally swept the Yankees from the field and then drove them in panic through the town of Gettysburg and up on the hills beyond.

During the battle of July second, our regiment was still held in reserve to guard the wagon trains. All that day we were in the vicinity of the Lutheran Theological Seminary on Seminary Ridge. Even though enlisted men were not allowed up in the cupola of the building, unless they were signalmen, we still had a commanding view of the action on July 2nd.

Although gravely concerned, we were greatly heartened to see the tenacious veterans of Lt. Gen. James Longstreet's First Corps march steadily past our encampment on Willoughby Run. We were especially gratified to see our fellow soldiers from the old Magnolia State, commanded by our brave and illustrious Gen. William Barksdale, file by on the way to their start line for the attack.

Tensions mounted throughout the day of the 2nd of July as the two armies moved into position and prepared to resume the bloodshed. At four p.m., the battle erupted in full fury when Longstreet's divisions surged forward and crashed into Federal forces on Little Round Top, at Devil's Den, in the Wheatfield, the Peach Orchard and along the Emmitsburg Road. The battle raged with unimaginable ferocity, the intensity of which claimed the lives of thousands of soldiers, regardless of private's worth or general's rank. The sounds of battle filled the air as the 11th Mississippi, commanded by Colonel Francis M. Green, finally arrived on the field from Cashtown. General Davis was greatly relieved to see our veteran troops and our presence bolstered the morale of his officers and men. The 11th was, perhaps, his finest regiment and one that was known for more than its fighting ability. One Mississippian noted, "Perhaps no regiment entered the service with a larger number of professional men in its ranks. Physicians were especially represented, both officers and privates. A member of the regiment boasted, "The 11th was made up of large measure from the choicest spirits in the state - intelligent, honorable and brave, and was a tried and trained body that won fame upon many bloody fields before Gettysburg." Indeed, these Mississippians had seen action on many fields and their numbers were indicative of past performance. When we arrived at Gettysburg, the 11th

TITHES OF BLOOD

Mississippi mustered only 350 men but we were battle-hardened veterans.

That night around the campfire the news came in on the rumor mill. Our beloved General Barksdale had been slain during his charge through the peach orchard directly to our front. We also heard a rumor that our division commander, Gen. Henry Heth, was in a bad way from a head wound and that Gen. Johnston Pettigrew of North Carolina had temporarily replaced him as our new division commander.

With the contest still unsettled, we knew that we would again be called upon to bear the brunt on the morrow. We four Wilkins boys shared a small fire and pathetically meager rations that night. Henry brought out his whetstone and began sharpening his D guard fighting knife. "Boys," he began, "do you all remember all of that fuss and fanfare when we mustered in at Crawford, all that elocutin', good food and pretty girls singing." "Yea, I thought we was off on a lark," added Charlie, "with the governor and all of them other pumped up politicians spoutin' off about bravery and the grandeur of war. Things ain't so grand now are they? We're all sick and starving and them Yankees just always keep on a' comin' no matter how many of 'um we shoot."

Sleep was very difficult that night and many prayers for deliverance from death were said to the Almighty. Some were to be answered but the majority were not. All night long the Yankees lobbed shells into our area to keep us awake.

Right before dawn on the morning of July 3, 1863 a

sudden and tremendous rattle of musketry opened over on our left on the back side of Culp's Hill. We soon learned that Ewell had finally decided to attack but this soon sputtered out and was shortly over. We all wished it had been Stonewall instead of Ewell making the attack!

Scattered everywhere were crumpled blue and grey clad bodies, dead horses, shattered timbers, wagons and cannon carriages, burned barns and farm houses. Small arms littered the hillsides along with ammo boxes and letters from loved ones recently freed from dead pockets by the body scavengers in search of money and valuables.

While we waited up on Seminary Ridge, we also took advantage of the lull and "acquired" ourselves some good shoes, hard tack, gum blankets and wool blankets off the Yankee dead that still lay about. The young "darkeys" of the University Greys lolled in the sunshine, or slumbered peacefully unaware,

Lt. Gen. Richard Ewell

like us, of the bloody work ahead. About ten o'clock in the fore noon, the Yankee Batteries over on Cemetery Ridge began lobbing well-aimed shells into our position.

About eleven o'clock our regiment was formed up and marched some several hundred yards back to the left and passed our fellow Mississippians of Gen. Carnot Posey's brigade on the way. We then took up a position in a skirt of thick hardwood forest known as McMillan's Woods. We were then halted and commanded to rest in place. Since we could still see those same dastardly Yankee cannon batteries on the ridge across the way, as soon as we were commanded to be at ease, we distributed ourselves around to our best advantage to avoid future cannon fire. Some of us dug fox holes; some hid behind trees and stumps in order to make ourselves as safe as possible with the means and time at our command. We then prepared to wait out the coming storm.

Staff officers and couriers soon began thundering in and out of our command post on lathered horses so we knew something big was afoot.

General Lee had finally decided to attack the Yankee center on Cemetery Ridge a mile across the way. He was right now lining up all of his available troops for a grand charge. From right to left facing the Yankee line would be Maj. Gen. George Pickett's division made up of the brigades of Brig. Gen. James L. Kemper, Gen. Dick Garnett and Brig. Gen. Lewis A. Armistead. To the left of Pickett are our units all under General Pettigrew (formally General Heth). These units from the left are Colonel Robert M.

Mayo and Colonel John M. Brokenborough's Virginians. Next came our regiment under Brig. Gen. Joseph R. Davis, then Colonel James K. Marshall, then Colonel Birkett D. Fry in command of Archer's Brigade. This whole front line was backed up by Trimble's double brigade.

Throughout the morning hours, scores of artillery pieces commanded by Colonel E. Porter Alexander were wheeled into position to our front and unlimbered. Ammunition chests were replenished and the gunners installed their brass sights on the cannon barrels and took note of the range to the enemy batteries across the way over on Cemetery Ridge.

While the artillery preparations were going on, the infantrymen of Pickett's, Pettigrew's and Trimble's many regiments were being brought onto the "start-line" position in McMillan's Woods.

During this emplacement time, the artillery fire from the Union guns into our lines was just awful. For two hours the fire was heavy and unceasing. Since we were directly behind the batteries, the Yankee counter-battery fire fell right into our ranks and the atmosphere suddenly became a shrieking, bellowing pandemonium of shells and flying fragments and death.

Directly Colonel E. Porter Alexander ordered our massed batteries to fire and the concussions were deafening. The soldiers of our brigade, laying prone in the woods, suffered greatly from the heat and suffocating smoke since the temperature up on the hill that day reached 87 degrees and the trees permitted little circulation of air. We suffered from thirst, also. To ease our suffering, my friend, Pvt. Walter W. Scales from Macon, was placed on water detail since he still limped badly from the serious wound he incurred at Sharpsburg. Anxious lest he should miss the charge, Scales called for a volunteer to take his place. Privates Charles S. Cooper and William Broadfoot volunteered. Neither one returned in time for the charge. Scales was wounded again in the charge and disabled for ninety days.

About this time a shell screamed down through the trees and struck the ground right in front of where my close family friend, Lt. Daniel Featherston, of Macon was lying. In total awe-struck horror, I saw the shell ricochet, entering his chest and blowing him ten feet in the air and twenty feet from where he had been lying.

Even though I knew he would die, I quickly grabbed another volunteer stretcher bearer and we swiftly took Dan back to the 11th's aid station manned by Dr. Joseph Holt. I suspected the worst and, sure enough, my friend breathed his last right there on Dr. Holt's operating table.

Before I could return to my Company E, however, a scene occurred that was so tragic and so soul-wrenching that it must be related here.

Just as I turned tearfully to leave, another set of stretcher bearers were coming in the door of the aid station. On the stretcher was my old friend and the pride of the University Greys, Jeremiah "Jere" S. Gage from the Richland Community near Lexington, Mississippi.

Dr. Holt wrote the following account for our regimental

107

history:

"Presently the wounded began to come in crouchingly; for many were killed and wounded before the charge began. The first to arrive, borne on a litter, was a princely fellow and favored son of the 11th Mississippi. I saw in an instant a condition of terrible shock. Keeping everybody close to the ground, I turned to him and he pointed to his left arm. I quickly exposed it and found that a cannon ball had nearly torn it away between the elbow and the shoulder. I made some encouraging remark when he smiled and said: 'Why, doctor, that is nothing; here is where I am really hurt,' and he laid back the blanket and exposed the lower abdomen torn from left to right by a cannon shot, largely carrying away the bladder, much intestine, and a third of the right half of the pelvis; but in both wounds so grinding and twisting the tissues that there was no hemorrhage. I then surveyed his personality, observing the tender devotion on the part of his litter bearers, and I saw a singularly attractive creature. Through his deathly pallor I could detect a sunburned blond, who in health would show a strong and ruddy countenance; a large head with a tousled shock of reddish golden locks like a mane, with the musculature and form of an athlete. Deferentially polite, there was something singularly self-confident and manly about him, answering distinctly the descriptive marks of that Shepherd, the younger son of Jesse about the time he chose five smooth stones out of the brook. 'For he was ruddy and withal of a beautiful countenance, and goodly to look to.'

TITHES OF BLOOD

"Without the slightest change of voice, he asked, 'Doctor, how long have I to live?' 'A very few hours,' I replied, 'You dear, noble fellow, I will see to it that you shall die easy.'

"No word or detail of this scene has faded from my memory. There was no thought of the dramatic; it was dreadfully genuine and naturally spontaneous, in the unconscious creating and acting of a grander tragedy than we might ever hope to play.

"I called for, and my hospital knapsack bearer, Jim Rowell, quickly handed me a two ounce bottle of black drop - a concentrated solution of opium, much stronger than laudanum.

"I poured a tablespoonful of it into a tin cup, with a little water, and offered it; but before his hand could reach it, a thought flashed into my mind, and withdrawing the cup, I asked, 'Have you no message to leave?'

"It startled him, and in a low moaning wail, he cried: 'My mother, O, my darling mother, how could I have forgotten you? Quick! I want to write.'

"By that time, all who were crouching under the low shelter were crowded around, oblivious of their own injuries and weeping silently.

"I took my seat on the ground close beside him and lifted him over, reclining on my chest, his face close to mine to steady his head, his right elbow in the hollow of my right hand to support and steady his arm, and a pencil slipped into his hand; Jim Rowell had provided the sheet of paper, held on the smooth lid of the hospital knapsack improvised as a desk. He wrote rapidly - all of this transpired in haste - murmuring to himself the words, audible to me for I looked another way.

"He began with place and date - 'On the Gettysburg battlefield, July 3rd, 1863.

'My dear Mother

'This is the last you may ever hear from me. I have time to tell you that I died like a man. Bear my loss as best you can. Remember that I am true to my country and my greatest regret at dying is that she is not free and that you and my sisters are robbed of my worth, whatever that may be. I hope this will reach you and you must not regret that my body can not be obtained. It is a mere matter of form, anyhow.

'This is for my sisters, too, as I can not write more. Send my dying release to Miss Mary . . . you know who.

J. S. Gage
Co. A, 11th Miss.

Mrs. P. W. Gage
Richland,
Holmes County,
Miss.
This letter is stained with my blood.'

"The last line he softly repeated aloud: 'I dip this letter in my dying blood.' With that he turned down the blanket and seizing the letter pressed the back of it upon his oozing, bloody wound, and handed it to me; giving his mother's address and begging to be sure she got that letter.

"From Virginia I saw that she got the letter, its content unrevealed except to herself.

"I arose from the ground and had him supported, when he turned to me with a reminder of my promise and of his hopeless pain. I handed him the cup and he feebly waved it saying: 'Come around, boys, and let us have a toast. I do not invite you to drink with me, but I drink the toast to you, and to the Southern Confederacy, and to victory!' And he drank it to the last drop, returning the cup, saying, 'I thank you.'

"We laid him back on some improvised soft head-rest, and I rushed off to work among the wounded.

"In about an hour, passing hastily, I lifted the cover from his face, to find him sleeping painlessly.

"As Jere neared death, he roused again and called for his comrades; 'Boys, come near me; it's growing dark. I can't see you. Come round me and take my hand; I want you to bury me...I want to be buried like my comrades. But deep, boys, deep, so the beasts won't get me.'

"Three hours later, as the tide of battle turned and the Southern Confederacy had touched its highest watermark and ebb-tide began, I passed again and laid aside the cover from his face, to find that the spirit of our reincarnated Sir Galahad had taken its flight in triumphal ascension to Him who instituted and consecrated the Holy Grail. Oh, the excruciating pathos and very agony of the glory!

"His death surpassed in tenderness of love, in

philosophical resignation, in courage and willing sacrifice of self, if it were possible, even that of Socrates, as revealed to us in the Phaedo.

"Gettysburg Penn.
July 3rd"

Sgt. Jeremiah "Jere" S. Gage
of the University Greys

TITHES OF BLOOD

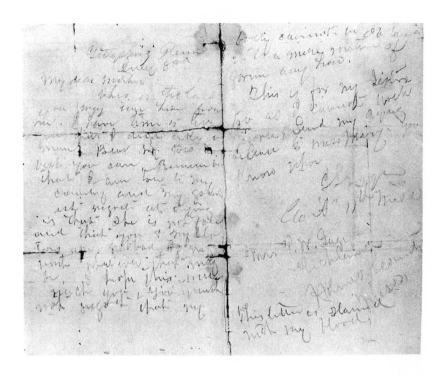

Gettysburg Penn.
July 3rd

My dear Mother

This is the last you may ever hear from me. I have time to tell you that I died like a man. Bear my loss as best you can. Remember that I am true to my country and my greatest regret at dying is that she is not free and that you and my sisters are robbed of my worth whatever that may be. I hope this will reach you and you must not regret that my body can not be obtained. It is a mere matter of form anyhow.

This is for my sisters too as I can not write more. Send my dying release to Miss Mary . . . you know who.

J. S. GAGE
Co. A, 11th Miss.

Mrs. P. W. Gage
Richland,
Holmes County,
Miss.

(This letter is stained with my blood.)

113

The Pickett-Pettigrew Charge
Chapter X

For two solid hours the deadly duel between Rebel and Yankee artillery continued. That awful line of Union cannon was the devil's pipe organ on which he played his hell-bent fugue while all of the demons in hell danced with fiendish glee. The soldiers in our brigade, lying prone in McMillan's Woods, suffered greatly from the awful heat and the acrid, suffocating smoke from the Yankee shell bursts and from the smoke from our own cannon. The temperature that afternoon was 87 degrees but it seemed much hotter. We were all dying from thirst and that is a very bad condition for a soldier to be in anytime; especially when he has been called upon to charge a mile through hell.

The maddened bomb shells continued to explode in every direction; before, behind, above and in our midst, scattering their projectiles in every direction, tearing away whole tops of stately oaks and killing and maiming our boys with random efficiency.

First you would hear the boom of the Yankee cannon,

Gen. George E. Pickett

then a high pitched screaming *whicker, whicker, whicker,* which struck terror in your heart like random death. Such a tornado of projectiles has seldom been the misfortune of anyone to see. The atmosphere was broken by the rushing solid shot and the shrieking shell; the sky, just now so bright, was at the same moment lurid with flame and murky with smoke. The sun at noontime was obscured by clouds of sulphurous mist, eclipsing the light and shadowing the earth in a funeral pall, which wrapped this field of blood in the darkness of death. Fiery fuses, like wild meteors of a heavenly wrath, hurdled with the discordantly screaming shells, causing mangled death and mutilation in its most horrible form.

Although our captain usually scattered out brothers in a

Confederates waiting in McMillian's Woods for the end of the artillery duel

unit, on this day we Wilkins boys were huddled close together in the awful shrapnel storm. I looked at my brothers. Each was filthy, dirty and ashen pale with deep circles under his eyes and chapped and cracked lips from the acrid smoke and bitter thirst. Our once-proud uniforms were now dingy, dirt streaked rags with filthy, ashen-white skin protruding from numerous holes. Our shoes were done for and the soles were tied on with green leather thongs cut from dead horses and cows on the battlefield. Our once-proud black "Jeff Davis" hats with the left brim pinned up with a star were rain-warped and bedraggled but we still had them on as our last symbol of personal defiance.

We all sensed the desperate nature of this mission today.

Davy crawled over to me. "This is it, ain't it, Tom?" "Naw, we been through much worse," I lied. "Pleas Goolsby just returned from a little scout out to our guns. He says we are to charge over a mile across an open field and then attack the blue-bellies who are entrenched behind a stone wall," replied Henry.

That news knocked the chocks out from under me and I had a weak feeling in the pit of my stomach. "Oh, we'll roust 'em out like we did at Gaines Mill," I replied, but the awful gnawing thirst and the total helplessness of our situation took hold of me. At home at Sunnyside we always hold hands when we have the blessing so right now we did just that. I cleared some cannon powder out of my throat. "Lord, deliver all of the Wilkins boys alive and unhurt through the upcoming battle and, like Reverend Hearn said so long ago, May it be the Yankees and not us who offer up tithes of blood today.' Amen."

We all felt a little better after that and seemed to grit our teeth with renewed determination.

A sudden stillness fell over the battlefield with depressing finality. The air was sulfurous and heavy as if all life had gone out of it.

My mind, in brief repose, turned to thoughts of "Sunnyside". Right now Papa was turning old Nell out to pasture after plowing the garden. Mamma was churning butter on the back porch and all the chickens were pecking in the yard. The sweet fragrance of wisteria and gardenias fill the air. How I wished to be there right now!

After a day lived in hell, at 3:10 P.M. we finally heard the bugles sound and the commands were barked down our

Brig. Gen. Joseph R. Davis

lines. 12,500 Confederate soldiers sprang to attention. Our own Captain H. P. Halbert of Macon stepped out of our combat ranks from his right front position, turned about face, and yelled, "for our sovereign State of Mississippi, for your homes, your mothers and sisters, men, do your duty this day!"

Our brigade commander over the 11th Mississippi,

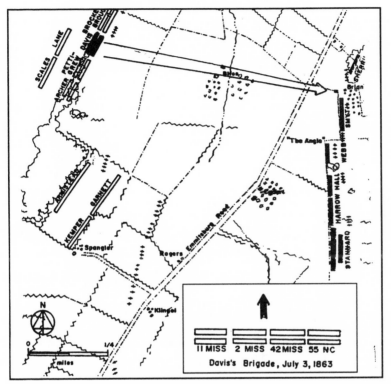

The position of Davis' Brigade, July 3

Brig. Gen. Joseph R. Davis, was posted immediately to our right. He was thirty-eight and small and dapper with his rakish "goatee with royals". President Davis' nephew, he had left a "cushy" staff job with the President for field duty with his fellow Mississippians. He usually had a "fighting cock" posture before a battle but right now he looked more like a "dying calf in a thunderstorm". He turned with his sword drawn and came slowly down the line. He stopped briefly in front of our flag and pointed his sword up to the sky as if to divine some heavenly intervention. We thought he

119

was going to give us a word of exhortation, but then he pointed his sword to the ground and said not a word. He just stood there, head down, knocking pebbles out of the path with the tip of his sword and looking like a shot fieldlark.

As we lined up in battle formation, I chanced a glance behind me. There on the road that ran through McMillan's Woods were all three of our main generals; General Lee in his full dress uniform on Traveler looking elegant but tense, our Corps commander, Gen. A. P. Hill, in his red battle shirt but pale and gaunt from a raging kidney infection and our new substitute division commander, Gen. Johnston Pettigrew, looking scholarly but excited.

We then shouldered our rifles and dressed on our beloved battle flag that had led us through many rough fights. She was a third bunting ANV issue flag and her battle honors

Brig. Gen. J. Johnston Pettigrew

were Manassas, Seven Pines, Gaines Farm, and Malvern Hill. Our lovely old flag snapped sharply over the finest group of young men that I have ever known. This included my three dear brothers that stood in rank beside me on that day of all days. All of our officers drew their swords, all of us clicked on our firing caps and fixed bayonets. We were ready!

120

TITHES OF BLOOD

Then the bugles blared and the drums beat the dreaded "long roll." "Forward march!" and we stepped out with battle flags and hearts flying in magnificent array. With perfectly dressed grey lines and polished rifles and swords flashing in the sunlight, we presented a grand and inspiring sight. Our cannoneers ceased firing as we swept through their batteries and they lustily cheered us on our way to our appointment with destiny.

Breaking into the sunlight we had an excellent view of the Yankee positions and their ominous batteries but never for a moment did we cower. Our men bore up bravely to the measure of their duty. We soon descended to the open fields that lay between us and the enemy and found the ground covered with clover as soft as a Turkish carpet.

We were going up now and all the forces of heaven and hell could not hold us back. Pinched-faced farm boys plucked from drab anonymity by fate and bombastic politicians would now expiate the sin of secession in mankind's most votive sacrament----blood.

Even in our abject weariness, hunger and dejection, we somehow sensed the magnitude of the up-coming deed. The power of the moment lay heavily upon us, but also quickened our step and spirit.

With perfectly dressed ranks we marched ever forward in the grandest charge ever recorded in human history and the destiny of the world hung in the balance.

Our lines beneath our lovely battle flags advanced across the deadly fields in perfect cadence. The Yankees must have

THE PICKETT-PETTIGREW CHARGE

The 11th Mississippi approaching the Brian Barn in the Pickett-Pettigrew Charge by Dale Gallon

been awed by the spectacle because the Union gunners did not hinder our advance at first. We only heard the whiz of occasional sniper fire and not a cannon was fired at us until we reached a strong post and rail fence along the Emmitsburg Road about a quarter of a mile from the enemy position. When we hit the fence, however, all hell broke lose and we were met by a heavy fire of grape, canister and exploding shells from Osborn's 32 gun battery which sadly took its toll on our ranks.

Right past the fence, a huge explosion hit the Prairie Guards. I was knocked out from the concussion. The first thing I remember when I came too was trying to find our unit in all of the smoke and hail of fire. I ran forward in a daze and up ahead I saw a few of my friends. When I caught up, I looked for my three brothers. I finally found Charlie. "That shell killed both Davy and Henry," he sobbed. That news staggered me further. Nothing has ever hit me like that before or since.

The concussion had blown my Enfield away but I soon picked up another. "You blue-bellied bastards!" I screamed, and charged on with my pitifully few comrades straight into that maelstrom of screaming chunks of shot and shell as 80 of the Yankee's big guns opened up on us along with the awful flanking small arms fire from the 8th Ohio and the 126th New York. That rifle fire spattered on the fence rails like heavy rain. Edgell's New Hampshire battery of 6 guns then opened up, firing diagonally into our left flank.

Pvt. William O'Brien of Company C, the Prairie Rifles,

was the color bearer of our beloved old battle flag at the start line. In the field behind the Brian barn, a twelve pounder howitzer round with cut fuse exploded directly above his shoe tops. He and the flag were blown skyward in a macabre dance of death. He hit the ground ten yards from me stone dead and several of the "University Greys" rushed to pick up the flag. The first to grab it was Tom McKie. Tom was out of himself by then and was operating on some ancient guidance in that maelstrom of lunacy, sound, dust, smoke

and death. Although since first Manassas he had spent every waking moment trying to avoid this very moment, the Thor he had now become was a cog in the larger monster of war. Instead of the sword of St. George, he carried a holier relic for that moment, the St. Andrew's Cross with stars. He had never screamed the Rebel Yell before but he was now--

Thomas Fondren McKie killed at Gettysburg

eeeeeeeeeooooooheeeoooh. . .

whump, a minie ball struck his breast, the wind was knocked out of him, but he felt no pain; the ground was spinning, he hit hard, the flag went down and he was at last back in the camellia scented garden with his mother in Oxford, Mississippi.

TITHES OF BLOOD

For seconds our battle flag fluttered across his gently paling baby face on that tortured hill but quickly, Pvt. James M. Griffin of Company H, the Chickasaw Guards grabbed for the flag but Joseph M. Smith of Company H seized the standard and raised it high. As we looked to our left flank, we saw to our horror, the 8th Ohio and the 125th New York charge into a full flank attack against Brokenborough's Brigade. Half of Brokenborough's troops were already cowering in a swale back behind us and those that were left couldn't take the heat so they tucked tail and skedaddled back to McMillan's Woods. Without Brokenborough, we men of the Prairie Guards had the dubious honor of being the left flank.

About this time the 8th Ohio, 1st Massachusetts and the 126th New York began firing double volleys at us from the left flank with all they had. Our boys were falling in heaps all along the line. Pleas Goolsby fell with a chest wound. The only escape was to run forward, which we did. I grieved for my two brothers but now I was just trying to survive. We re-grouped a little around our flag and continued toward an ominous black stone wall that was belching fire and brimstone at us through the acrid smoke.

Woodruff's six Napoleons now opened up, raking us with deadly canister shot. From this point, forward, each man was pretty much on his own hook. We were being pounded as no soldiers had ever been before. Instead of the ole Rebel Yell, I could hear an awful sound rise above the tumult. It was a huge collective moan pumping out from deep inside our poor boys. It was the worst sound that I have ever heard before or since.

By now we were coming up behind the Brian Barn. The stone wall ran into the sides of the barn. From our right the Yankee Infantry was standing and delivering volley after volley into our pitifully thin ranks. When we got near the barn, the Yanks from the 12th New Jersey riddled us with buckshot and ball which blinded and maimed as well as killed our boys. Our brave captain, Henry Halbert, fell dead about then, his sword still defiantly pointed at the enemy.

Just then, something hit me in the right thigh, and I spun to the ground. I blacked out from the numbing pain but quickly came to, laying just to the right of the Brian barn with a broken leg. I had a scorching thirst and the awful pain made my whole body throb. When my vision cleared I saw two of my friends from the Noxubee Rifles, John J. Howell and his brother Frank A. Howell, reach the stone wall. John went over but was captured. I soon saw John J. Howell stagger back to our lines wounded but alive. Two more Prairie Guard boys, John T. Morgan and John Lewis Sherman, reached the wall. Sherman was wounded but Morgan, who was miraculously unhurt, brought him back. Morgan was the only member of the Prairie Guards that was not a casualty in the charge.

From my position while laying behind the Brian Barn, I caught an occasional glimpse of the sad remnants of our regiment as they dashed the final yards to the wall and to destruction.

TITHES OF BLOOD

I saw Captain J. T. Stokes of Company F shot down twenty steps from the wall. Then Captain George Bird of Company K and Captain William Thomas Magruder, brother of Gen. John B. "Prince John" Magruder were both shot dead while cheering some of their men over the wall.

Right then, all of the Yankees in four lines rose up behind the wall, and on command of their Gen. Alexander Hays, poured terrible volleys into our pitifully thinned ranks. Soon, most of our regimental officers were either killed, wounded or captured. It then became a soldier's battle, in which our watchword "The grave of a hero or victory" was being gloriously exemplified.

As the smoke cleared a bit, I saw the last of Company A, the University Greys, come up. Charging with a Rebel Yell, the few undaunted survivors impetuously rushed through that hell of fire and most were instantly shot down. Second Lt. John V. Moore was out in front, facing the ragged survivors of our regiment and trying to close up the fearful gaps being cut into our line, when Pvt. Andrew J. Baker of the "Greys" shouted "For God's sake, John, order charge!" and the thin grey line rushed forward to the stone wall and immortality.

With the last burst of resolve and all alone, the last member of the University Greys churned into his final earthly act; a bullet drilled his right leg, he falls and rolls and is up once again. Another bullet hits his right shoulder, acrid white smoke blasts out from the volley, but still he charges into the steel hurricane.

THE PICKETT-PETTIGREW CHARGE

As the smoke clears a bit between volleys he spies the ominous dark grey stone wall and with all of the might of the doomed, he lunges forward and then the world becomes thunder and he is beyond pain. His still churning legs gradually cease to move as he falls across the wall. Merciful death claims the last student from Oxford.

All of the companies were now jumbled. Regimental Staff Sergeant William O'Brien was cut down just short of the wall. Pvt. James M. Griffin of Company H stooped down and reached for the flag but was shot in the foot. Pvt. Joseph M. Smith made two steps forward but was shot through the mouth. Pvt. William P. Marion of the Chickasaw Guards picked it up, took two steps toward the wall and was shot dead.

Four brave men had died beneath that precious battle flag, its shattered flag staff still held in the clutch of death, but without one moment's pause, that brave and never flinching little Irishman, Joseph Marable, pried that dear tattered battle flag from Private Marion's devoted dead hands and held it high. Although the staff was shot in two the flag still dangled in brave defiance from only the top corner which was still tied to the top of the staff. With super-human effort, Marable planted our battle flag on the stone wall and was instantly hit from the side by a clubbed musket and fell across the wall unconscious but not critically wounded. The flag, in a gesture of despair, suddenly sank down as if dying. Sergeant Maggi of the Garibaldi Guards of New York City later seized the battle flag to the loud hurrahs of his mess mates.

Several of our boys came staggering back toward the back of the Brian Barn and they helped me back over that shot-plowed, body strewn field.

When we got back down to the Emmitsburg Road, I saw to my dismay my close friend, Second Lt. Pleas Goolsby laying on his back, staring up at the sky with blank sightless eyes. A big hole was in his chest and his breath came in faint, convulsive snorts which expelled a pinkish-red froth from his mouth, nose and the hole itself, covering most of his upper torso with bloody foam. "The flag," he murmured, "Did we save the flag?" Then the last blood bubble burst on his blackened lips and his head flopped over. He was dead but it sure was hard to leave him out there in no-man's land. A fond memory flooded over me of Pleas, so boyish and proud as he paraded our new flag around the drill field at our mustering-in ceremony back at Crawford, an age ago. Lord! War sho' ain't what it's cracked up to be!

As I cripped my way back down that dreadful hill, back to our start line in McMillan's Woods, I saw the saddest sight I have ever seen. All of the little black servants owned by the University Greys were standing in a row wringing their hats in their hands, with tears streaming down their

Uniform of the Garibaldi Guards

dusty cheeks. Each boy cried out his master's name, but no master answered. The University Greys had ceased to exist. They were all gone - gone to glory up on Cemetery Ridge.

Before I went to the field hospital to get my broken leg set, I searched for and found my brother, Charlie. He was powder burned and frazzled but my joy at finding him alive was indescribable.

We just hugged each other and cried for ten minutes. That is all that we could do. This day was so much more than a mere tithe of blood for our family and for the Southern Confederacy. It was the beginning of the end.

On the 4th of July 1863 Vicksburg surrendered while the opposing armies at Gettysburg glowered at each other from ridges scarcely a mile apart. Union Commander Maj. Gen. George Gordon Meade contented himself with occupying Gettysburg and sending out patrols and burial parties. Men with time to spare walked out on the field of battle. One of

Looking for a friend

the boys in a burial detail described the unforgettable scene, "Upon the open fields, like sheaves bound by the reaper, in crevices of the rocks, behind fences, trees and buildings, in thickets where they had crept for safety only to die in agony; by stream or wall or hedge, wherever the battle had raged or their weakening steps could carry them, lay the dead. Some, with faces bloated and blackened beyond recognition, lay with glassy eyes staring up at the blazing sun; others, with faces downward and clenched hands filled with grass or earth, which told of the agony of their last moments. Here a headless trunk, there a severed limb or human head; in all the grotesque positions that unbearable pain and intense suffering contorts the human form, they lay. Upon the faces of some, death had frozen a smile; some showed the trembling shadow of fear, while upon others was indelibly set the grim stamp of determination. All around was the wreck the battle storm leaves in its wake - broken caissons, dismounted guns, small arms bent and twisted by the storm or dropped and scattered by disabled hands; dead and bloated horses, torn and ragged equipment, and all the sorrowful wreck that the waves of battle leave at their ebb; and overall, hugging the earth like a fog, poisoning every breath, the pestilential stench of decaying humanity.

~~~~~~~~~~

Historians have devoted pages to the description of Pickett's gallant charge. It is well, such deeds should never be forgotten, but it was also the Pettigrew charge. The

THE PICKETT-PETTIGREW CHARGE

Union dead west of the Seminary

Confederate dead near McPherson's Woods

records of Company E, 11th Mississippi show that our company went into battle with 39 men, and of that number, all were killed or wounded, save one man. I lost two of my brothers; Davy Crockett Wilkins and Henry Martin Wilkins, who died one on either side of me, and I was terribly wounded in the leg. John T. Morgan was the only man able for duty the rest of that day. Those who were badly wounded were left in the field hospital and were captured when our army fell back. Those who were able to walk or bear transportation in wagons were sent back to Virginia in what was called the wounded train, which was escorted by Imboden's Calvary.

I was in one of the hospital wagons and the trip back to Virginia was totally excruciating and I blacked out many times from the pain of my leg wound made much worse by the jolting and lurching of the wagon. The screams of the badly wounded was a living nightmare without end.

At one part of the road, the enemy's cavalry captured about a dozen wagons which were loaded with wounded. J. D. Love, one of our company, was among those taken prisoner. Lee's army retired from Gettysburg on the night of the 5th and the next day took position at Hagerstown to allow time to lay a pontoon bridge across the Potomac at Falling Waters. The train crossed the Potomac at Williamsport and went on to Winchester.

The appearance of the ragged and worn Army of Northern Virginia, nicknamed "Lee's Miserables", on the retreat was prepossessing in one respect only. Our muskets were clean and our bayonets bright, and a firm and undaunted spirit everywhere abounded. With clothing dirty and ragged, shoes worn and broken, and hats dilapidated and covered with dust, we came homeward-bound with jests, jokes and repartee that enlivened the march even under such distressing conditions. Twitted on his shaggy attire by one of a group of residents gathered on the roadside to see the Rebels pass, the jolly Neely Nance of Company F, the Noxubee Rifles, of the 11th Mississippi apologetically explained that in the South, it was the custom to put on one's worst clothes on "hog-killing days".

When the 11th Mississippi was passing through the town of Greencastle, Pennsylvania a bevy of local lovelies stood on the sidewalk waving American flags. Two of the more well-endowed nymphets had crossed the flags around their upper torsos. As "The Prairie Guards" marched past, ole H. B. Tharp couldn't stand it. Seeing this demonstration of hostility by the fairer sex, he broke ranks and approached them. "See here, girls, youens better take off them durned flags because we ole Rebels er hell on breast-works!"

The retreat from Gettysburg

The last of our troops crossed on the evening of the 14th with a loss of a few

Confederates at a ford

men in battle there, but one of the men was our own beloved General Pettigrew, who brilliantly directed the rear guard action against Brig. Gen. George A. Custer and his blood thirsty Sixth Wisconsin Cavalry.

After crossing the Potomac, and scrambling up the bank, Pvt. Gabriel N. Smither, of Company G, the Lamar Rifles, of the 11th Mississippi, in passing the regimental band, said to the leader, "Stewart, by blood, play Dixie." Soon the quick notes of that ever inspiring air wafted upon the breeze, when followed a roll of the Rebel Yell of defiance that meant too plainly to the enemy on the other side of the river that there was yet remaining strength, determination and fight in the Army of Northern Virginia. To Heth's division, of which we veteran soldiers of Mississippi had formed an integral part, belonged the honor of fighting first at Gettysburg and last at Falling Waters, on the Potomac River.

The army retired to Winchester and shortly thereafter we went to Culpepper, Virginia. While we were in camp here we rested and had good victuals. My wound was treated daily and it steadily healed. H. A. Ervin was elected our Lieutenant. From here the army retired south of the Rapidan in the neighborhood of the Orange Courthouse.

THE PICKETT-PETTIGREW CHARGE

Longstreet's Corps was sent to reinforce Bragg at Chattanooga, and Ewell's and Hill's Corps had a grand review. Toward the middle of October, A. P. Hill marched his corps by a circuitous route for the purpose of getting into Mead's rear at Manassas. The enemy retreated but Hill attacked his rear guard on the 14th at the Battle of Bristol, Virginia. The division suffered considerable loss, but our company lost no men. In falling back from here we destroyed the railroad across the Rapahannock and we camped there long enough for our mail and supplies to reach us. That afternoon at mail call, I got this letter from Mama:

"Dear Tom,
    I just got your Capn.'s letter about the death of Davy and Henry. Mine and your Papa's hearts is broken. I can't do anything but hold old dog Cap'n in my lap and rock and remember. My second boy and my next youngest gone. I go to bed weeping and wake up weeping. Their isn't any sunshine at Sunnyside. I hope you and Charlie will be careful. Don't you two go leadin any charges or toten the flag. On July 3rd a freak storm blew in from the southeast and lightning hit the big catalpa tree by the smoke house that you boys' had carved your names on. It ripped like a curtain from top to bottom."

136

Resting on the Rapidan
Chapter XI

For a few days, we held the line of this river and then retired to our quarters south of the Rapidan. Here the division rested and recruited until the 6th of December when it was called upon to fight the Battle of Mine Run. The night before the battle our company was placed on a picket line and had orders to fire for a little while should the enemy advance the next morning and then fall back so as to draw him under fire of our batteries and against our works. In other words, to lure him into our trap. The Yankee attack was so feeble on our part of our line that we did not retire. Union General Fairchild was shortly after this observed reconnoitering in our front and was fired on and killed by one of our snipers. I was a sniper that day.

On another part of the field, the enemy advanced until our artillery opened on them and they retired. Thus ended the Battle of Mine Run. Mead re-crossed the river and Lee's army went into winter quarters around Orange Courthouse.

The quarters of the 11th Mississippi Regiment were about two miles south of town. We built cabins for ourselves out of logs with tents for roofs. We also built a church and a theater out of logs with split-plank roofs. Our regimental band directed by Professor Tomlinson of Company E composed a theatrical troop. I always thought that a theatrical troop was pretty sissy, but a lot of the guys kind of enjoyed it for something to do. Our favorite skit was: "What is the First Duty of a Surgeon? Under the names of drugs and medicines to purchase a full supply of good liquor. What is the second duty? To cause all private sellers to be searched, and all the good whiskey found there to be confiscated, lest the soldiers should find them and the whole army become drunk. What is the third duty? To see that the surgeon and his assistants drink up all of said liquor!"

The winter passed quietly except that on one occasion during very cold weather we were sent toward Madison, Virginia to meet a cavalry raid. Toward the end of March, we exchanged quarters with a North Carolina regiment and picketed a ford on the Rapidan.

Right after that we returned to our quarters and engaged in a tremendous snow ball fight. Gen. A. P. Hill, our corps commander, did not participate this winter. He looks very gaunt and sick and can barely mount his horse. We had one heck of a time, though. Several boys got black eyes, but we had a lot of fun.

Mostly, it was just boredom and trying to keep warm. Me and Charlie had one very upsetting occurrence happen. We were detailed to drive a troop wagon down to the troop train siding and pick up some new conscripts. The first boy off the train was our baby brother, John T. "I'm eighteen now," he blurted out and we couldn't help but hug him.

We all wrote home a lot. My best friend John Morgan shared this letter with me before he mailed it to his father in Noxubee County:

TITHES OF BLOOD

Battle of Gettysburg

Dear Daddy,

We went into the fight with 39 men and came out with only one left for duty. Fifteen of us were killed stone dead on the field and twenty-three placed *hors de combat*, and many other companies were in pretty much the same fix. We did all that it was possible for men to do. We fought to the bitter end and never worried until we were knocked from our feet. We made charge after charge the most fearful was ever known to the profession of arms. I was in every battle that my regiment was engaged in, and I never saw anything like that awful day, nor have I read of it in history.

There was fearful destruction on both sides and the hilltops and sides were heaped with mountains of the dead, no more to measure arms in this world.

All my company officers were swept to death or wounded, and when I marched out towards the Potomac, the lone man of our company, I wept that I was not slain with the rest of my dear comrades whom I loved like brothers and would have died for any of them. This day and this awful battle I can never forget, and those dear boys, many of whom lie somewhere in unknown graves. The memory of that awful day hangs on my memory as bright as if it was only yesterday. I, too, sought death that I might be with my comrades, but not a shot nor a shell ever came to relieve me, and I am here yet to ponder over the past and fight all those Virginia battles over again and weep for those dear comrades that are gone; and how I went through the whole war and never missed a battle and never received a wound is something mysterious to me. It might have been on account of the prayers of my mother, I don't know, for I was her baby boy.

There were 50,000 left on the field of both armies, and General Lee recrossed the Potomac with less than half of the men he had advanced with.

This, dear Daddy, is all I know of this awful day and the campaign that led to it.

John T. Morgan

Co. E., 11th Miss. Vols.

As Spring began to open, the Northern papers were filled with the exploits of General Grant who had taken over the Army of the Potomac and the newspapers predicted that Lee's little army would be overwhelmed by the first stroke of the "great hammerer' of the West, Gen. Ulysses S. Grant.

The Dreadful Wilderness
Chapter XII

On the 2nd of May, Gen. Robert E. Lee mounted Traveller, the seven-year-old "Confederate Grey", as Lee called his horse, and with his ranking officers, ascended Clark's Mountain, at 700 feet the highest lookout point available. Through the chilly fog of early morning an inspiring panorama unfolded. Curling around the foot of the mountain was the Rapidan River, brown, flat and 200 feet wide. Due east, about thirteen miles downstream was Germanna Ford, and a few miles farther, Ely's Ford. South of the fords sprawled a gray-green expanse called the wilderness, twelve miles wide and six miles deep.

If Grant could get his army swiftly through this nasty tangle of briars, ridges, hillocks, stunted pines and dense undergrowth, he could use his superior numbers to stall the Army of Northern Virginia in open country. Lee studied the terrain through his glasses and understood his opponent's strategy. Raising a hand encased in a leather gauntlet, he pointed eastward to the two river crossings and told his officers, "Grant will cross by one of those fords."

True to Lee's prediction, Grant crossed the Rapidan with his army on Lee's right flank at Germanna and Ely's Fords on the morning of May 4th and the army of the Potomac was on its seventh 'on to Richmond' march.

Up to now, we had whipped them every time. That same

day, our division, which was led by Gen. Henry Heth, moved down the road leading to the wilderness and we slept that night on Mine Run. The next morning our 11th Mississippi Regiment deployed across the road in the advance with a skirmish line thrown out, while the rest of our regiment followed in column.

We had an invigorating march to battle that day. Gen. Robert E. Lee spent the whole morning riding with our Division at the head of A. P. Hill's Corps. Soon after daylight the Union Cavalry was pushed out of the Parker's Store area. Soon afterwards the headquarters party consisting of Generals Robert E. Lee, A. P. Hill and J. E. B. Stuart and their staff officers rode up to a large field and

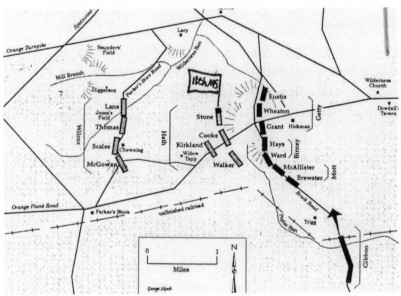

The Orange Plank Road front on May 5 at 4:30 p.m.

dismounted under the shade of some trees. We could see them over there from our battle line. Suddenly a strong force of Yankee skirmishers came out of the woods a short distance away. General Lee walked rapidly off toward our troops calling for Colonel Taylor to get out of there. General Stuart stood up and looked the danger square in the face. General Hill remained as he was. They were in pistol shot range of the Yankees. The flustered Federal officer gave the command "about face" and the Yankee troops disappeared into the timber. Finding themselves in the presence of Confederate troops, the Yankees were as surprised as we were.

Right after that occurrence, General Lee turned the fighting back over to Gen. Henry Heth, who was our division commander. He immediately shook out a skirmish line and I was one of the skirmishers. We tried to run the enemies' skirmishers off, but could not do so, so we all halted at sort of a standoff. The division came up and the line of battle was formed and all was quiet for an hour or more. We were astride a road called the Orange Plank Road. After we waited for about a hour with nothing going on, all of a sudden the Yankees charged

Maj.-Gen. Henry Heth

in force. We understood later that it was the troops of Union Gen. Alexander Hayes, who had opposed us on Cemetery Ridge at Gettysburg. General Hayes placed his brigade in front of us on Union Gen. George Getty's right flank. They charged us with a whoop and a holler, but got confused and tangled in the terrible underbrush. We flanked them on both flanks and Hayes waved his brigade forward in bits and pieces.

We boys on the firing line found the range of the massed Union troops and for some terrible minutes we almost wiped out the Yankees. The musketry was fearful, men fell on every side and our newly issued ANV battle flag received its share of bullets. Charge after charge was made by both sides against each other. Sometimes we drove back the Yankees and then they would rally and drive us back. At one point in front of our brigade, all of the bushes as large as a man's wrist were cut down two and one-half feet above the ground by musket balls. We fought like this for what seemed like an hour or more and finally all the troops, Yankees and Confederates alike, fell upon their guns in a sort of unspoken truce. During this lull in combat, our artillery was brought up via the plank road.

About that time, General Wilcox on our right committed the last two brigades of his division into the battle and they turned off the Plank Road and relieved us. Behind Thomas came five North Carolina regiments of Brig. Gen. James H. Lane's Brigade. These filed off south of the road. As the last troops available to Lee entered the battle, a North Carolinian of the 37th Regiment recalled that the whole regiment roared like Banshees.

The ground in front of us was covered with dead and wounded Yankees. It was so horribly dry that the parched underbrush was ignited by sparks and stroked by the wind. As the fires flared up all along the battle line, the wounded, screaming hideously, were burned to death in the flames. The flames exploded many of the cartridge boxes which were strapped to the bellies of the fallen wounded and blew bloody holes into their helpless whimpering bodies. The incessant pop of cartridges gave us only a horrible hint of the dreadful terror and unendurable pain which they suffered.

The burning woods, May 6 - rescuing the wounded

THE DREADFUL WILDERNESS

The bodies of the dead were blackened and burned beyond all possibility of recognition.

On the morning of the 6th, the enemy renewed the battle, while Kershaw's Division of Longstreet's Corps was relieving Heth's which was held in reserve that day. Some confusion was caused and our Brigade under Colonel Stone remained on the line and took a very active part in the severe battle that followed.

The fight was kept up desperately all afternoon until dark. When night came on the Yankees were on our left flank. Occasionally, in the bombs' red glare we could see the smoky black silhouettes of the enemy and we blazed away at them with impunity. The lines were, to some extent, re-formed after dark, which left General Wilcox with his division of four brigades on the left. Our brigade was temporarily commanded by Col. John M. Stone, of our 11th Mississippi Regiment while General Davis was away in Richmond.

General Longstreet with his corps had wintered on the Orange and Alexandria Railroad some two miles to the rear of Orange Courthouse. It was expected that Longstreet's command would arrive on the battlefield during the night of May 5. When daylight came, Longstreet's command had not arrived. Before sun-up on the morning of the 6th of May, the Federal troops made an assault on General Wilcox's left flank and the whole of that division broke and ran pell-mell down the line.

Our beloved 11th Mississippi commanded by Colonel

Stone, occupied the right of Gen. Heth's Division. After General Wilcox's division broke and came rushing down on Heth's line, Col. J. M. Stone held his four Mississippi Regiments in battle line, and changed front to meet the new Yankee onslaught.

He so fought and maneuvered us Mississippians as to hold back the entire Federal force for two hours. Colonel Stone had no support on either flank and at that time did not know whether there were any organized troops to relieve him. After an anxious and bloody two hours had passed, we heard General Longstreet's belated musketry over on our left flank. At this time Colonel Stone, with his four Mississippi Regiments, was in a position to act according to his own judgment. The balance of the division to which he belonged had broken and the division commander had gone back to reorganize them. When Longstreet's command moved into the fight on our left, there was an opening in the lines to the left of General Mahone's Brigade. Colonel Stone of his own volition filled up this gap and ordered charge. We drove the Yankees for some distance across the plank road to our right. At this critical moment General Longstreet was wounded, and there was a halt made in the Confederate lines.

Soon after the halt was made General Benning's Georgia Brigade passed in front of Col. J. M. Stone's Brigade. This again left Stone so that he could act as his judgment might dictate, and to his left there was an Alabama Brigade being heavily assaulted and was giving way. Stone saw this and moved his Brigade still containing his four Mississippi regiments in rear of the Alabama Brigade and ordered a charge. We went in with a whoop and a holler and drove the Yankees back until we occupied a position in advance of the other Confederate units.

Hoping the other units would move up to our lines, Colonel Stone ordered a halt and commanded us to pull all the logs within reach together to make a kind of a temporary breastwork. We had no shovels to fill in the holes but we loosened the dirt with our bayonets and threw it up on the breastworks with our tin cups and frying pans. Very few logs were to be had so we made a four foot high parapet out of fence rails and Yankee corpses. This was done in about twenty minutes. Then we hunkered down behind our grisly breastworks.

The boys were muttering nervously to each other while pulling their cartridge boxes around in front for easy access. A last swig was pulled from our canteens and firing caps were positioned at the top of the cap box. "Here they come," yelled Captain Ervin. All hammers were cocked back which made a strange little metallic ripping sound.

Then we saw the line of blue advancing through the tortured trees, as scared as we were. "Shoot low, be sure to aim, make each shot count," yelled our Captain, and then "Fire at will!" and the battle line erupted in a rumbling explosion of acrid smoke. Steel ramrods clanked on steel barrels amid the awful din of battle.

The Yankees had an entirely different battle cry from us; they went into the charge with a deep sounding HUZZAH which really didn't intimidate us like our Rebel Yell did them. They were yelling their Huzza now and we were trying to aim and fire, but in the thick smoke, we ofttimes just fired in the general direction of the Yankees.

John Allen screamed, grabbed his throat, and fell dead right by me, his crimson lifeblood pumping away into the Virginia soil and the sharp carborundum smell of human blood filled our nostrils. Yankees were falling like limp dishrags all along their line. Another "whump" sound and John Turner fell dead from his kneeling position on the firing line. The musketry was now an incessant sputter with horizontal stabs of flame licking out back and forth.

The Yankees were pumping so many men into the attack that we had to modify our battle tactics. Our best shots such as me and Charlie were designated as front line "sharpshooters" with three boys behind us as "loaders". I would see a Yankee materialize out of the fire and battle smoke, "bam!" I'd fire and immediately another loaded rifle was thrust into my hands, and another Yankee went to either a hospital or to a slit trench grave.

At first I was full of vengeance for Davy and Henry but after an hour of this, I grew violently sick from all the slaughter and had to be relieved by another sharpshooter.

After what seemed like an eternity, the sputtering rifle fire ceased on the Yankee side and we then knew that we had beat them back once again. During that afternoon the enemy assaulted us again with line after line, but we beat off every attack from behind the log and corpse breastworks we had thrown together so hastily. Although we had tried to shield our baby brother, John T. Wilkins suffered a painful but not mortal wound in his right "shooting" shoulder and he was sent home for the duration of the war.

It seemed to us boys on the death line that if the enemy had broken through the Confederate works and cut our corps in two, they might possibly have defeated the Confederate Army that day. I have always thought that it was fortunate for the Confederate Army that Colonel Stone was at liberty to act on his own judgment, on this particular occasion. Had he not relieved that Alabama Brigade the enemy would most assuredly have broken through the Confederate lines at this point on the Orange Turnpike Road.

After Colonel Stone had led the charge and relieved the Alabama Brigade, it left us in an advanced position in front of the Confederate lines. During the afternoon General Heth made a request of General Lee to relieve Colonel Stone and let him come back to his division. General Lee's reply was that Stone had gotten himself into that advanced position and would have to remain a while. During that afternoon our losses in Stone's 11th Mississippi Brigade were very heavy. Our Company E (The Prairie Guards) had two men killed and five wounded while resisting the frequent assaults of the enemy.

When night came the fighting ceased with the Yankees in very close proximity to us. General Lee deemed it necessary to strengthen his lines after dark, and issued orders to that effect and the lines were strengthened by withdrawing the troops from each flank of Colonel Stone's Brigade. But Stone, not being under the command of any general officer, did not get the order. When he sent his aides to each end of his brigade to see if he was connected he found that the troops had been withdrawn from both flanks and new lines established in his rear. We were liable to be fired on by our own troops and the enemy was in such close proximity that if we made any demonstration we were sure to be fired on from that direction. After the enemy commenced firing our troops in the rear would be sure to reply, and we, placed between the two lines, would have a bad situation. But Colonel Stone sent a courier back to the Confederate lines and notified the commander that he was out in front and would come out. So all of our troops along the line were notified. Then the order was given to move out cautiously and make as little noise as possible and get back behind the Confederate lines. Without any mishap, we boys of the 11th Mississippi took our dead comrades back to our main line of battle and buried them that night. After making sure that every man had pulled out, Colonel Stone joined the balance of his division.

The next morning, the 7th of May, General Heth with his staff rode to Colonel Stone and addressed him as the gallant Colonel, and said, "Colonel, you won your stars yesterday, the stars of a Brigadier-General."

Our regiment was held on the reserve line on May 7th, until late in the afternoon. Then it was moved to the front

THE DREADFUL WILDERNESS

In the wake of battle

line; but no fighting was done that day except picket fighting and cavalry skirmishes. Later that night when all signs of the conflict had ceased, there was heard, miles to our right, at first an indistinct sound, then becoming louder and louder as each Division passed it down the line, then dying away to our left until it was lost in the murmuring waters of the Rapidan. It was the Confederate Yell which told us that another victory had been won. It told General Grant that his supposed hammering process had only welded our line with a bond that transcends human comprehension.

The next morning a yellow, foul-smelling fog clutched at the tree tops while an eerie quiet pervaded our front. Toward noon as we prepared to vacate the battlefield, our Company E was ordered up for skirmish duty. We were deployed out in front of the 11th Mississippi.

As a sharpshooter in the regiment, I knew what I personally could do to a Yankee skirmisher at three hundred yards. For this reason, I always dreaded being a skirmisher. We were usually one to five hundred yards out in front of the regiment, totally exposed and scouting for trouble. This usually meant drawing the enemy's fire. On this quiet morning after the great battle, our entire company was on the prod.

We passed over the battlefield and by the enemies' field hospitals of the previous day and were surprised at the number of dead. The condition of the wounded was horrible. They were blown all to bits or burned beyond recognition. None of the wounded had been removed and many of them begged us to kill them and put them out of their misery. The day before we had watched in horror as a wounded Yankee slit his own throat as the flames approached.

I stopped briefly to give some water to a horribly burned Yankee when, WHUMP, the breath was knocked out of me, my legs seemed to die and the ground swirled up to meet my face and the pain-wracked world went black. Eons later, I heard our regimental surgeon, Dr. Joseph Holt's voice from far away. "Wilkins has a double lung wound, Captain Ervin, "His prospects for recovery are negligible but I'll try to find a kind family in this area who may wish to nurse him back to health.

At that very moment, I prayed to God to spare me and my prayers were answered. A kind family *did* take me in and, in due time, I totally recovered and re-joined my dear ole unit, the 11th Mississippi.

Further on, our boys came upon strong earth works along the road leading to Richmond, but they were deserted. The Yankees had flown our once deadly coop!

THE DREADFUL WILDERNESS

In this engagement Company E suffered the following losses: killed; John Allen, John Turner, wounded; Pete McGuire, B. B. Tomlinson, G. B. Triplett and me, Tom Wilkins.

Spottsylvania Courthouse
CHAPTER XIII

That evening Heth's Division started east for Spottsylvania Courthouse to block General Grant who had evacuated the Federal lines in our front and moved his army off in that direction, leaving thousands of his dead soldiers on the battlefield unburied.

General Lee was on the alert and moved almost simultaneously a portion of the Confederate Army to meet Grant's Army at any point that he might make demonstrations. Our division remained on the battlefield May 8, burying our Confederate dead until late in the afternoon. The sights and smells that assailed us were simply indescribable. Debris of battle covered the ground as far as the eye could see; rifles with shattered stocks, knapsacks, canteens, blankets ground into the soil, hats, letters fluttered all over the ground that dead eyes would never read again, chunks of shrapnel from exploded bombs were sticking in every tree and trench wall, dead horses lay in windrows along with the hideous corpses of the Union soldiers who lay in postures of agony. Some of the bodies were swollen to twice their normal size; others were shriveled; some of their faces, contorted in horror, were bloated and black, some were shrunken greenish-yellow. Most of them had a death induced contraction of the arm muscles which caused their hands to contract into bony claws which oftimes were held up above the body in morbid supplication. Some of the corpses burst asunder with the pressure of foul gases and vapors. . . . The odors were nauseating and so deadly that in a short time we all sickened and were lying with our mouths close to the ground, most of us vomiting profusely.

Later that day, General Heth moved his headquarters, followed by the main body of the Confederate Army, and we were held in reserve all day of the 9th. By the morning of the 10th of May, General Lee was convinced that General Grant was moving a body of troops in the direction of Beaver Dam Station on the Virginia Central Railroad, evidently with the intention of cutting off General Lee's supplies. Davis's Brigade, together with detachments from other commands, was put under command of General Early to meet the Federal forces that were moving towards Beaver Dam Station. General Early moved the command and got in between Beaver Dam Station and the Federal column. Company G (Lamar Rifles), 11th Mississippi Regiment, was detailed as brigade skirmishers under command of Captain Nelms. The Company was thrown forward and deployed as skirmishers to find the position of the enemy. The Lamar Rifles soon met those of the enemy and gradually drove them back until they encountered a mill pond.

The Yankee skirmishers had taken up their position on the opposite side of the pond from the Confederates, and the only way for our skirmishers to cross to the opposite side was to cross the creek on the mill dam. It was a difficult matter, deploying in the face of the Federal pickets. We

TITHES OF BLOOD

Confederates were assembled and crossed on the mill dam and by taking advantage of the bank that made a little rise, were enabled to deploy in the face of the enemy. Our Company E and several other companies joined the fray. After we were deployed we were immediately ordered forward, but had not gone far until it was discovered that the enemy's lines extended beyond our left flank, which made it necessary to extend intervals between skirmishers. This was done and all were again ordered forward. We Confederates charged and drove the enemy before us, until our troops on the right encountered a heavy force posted behind breastworks.

General Early formed his line of battle and ordered our troops to charge the enemy and drive them from the breastworks. Captain Nelms, in temporary command of us skirmishers as well as of the 11th Mississippi Regiment, crept up the ravine with his skirmishers and soon found that his command was on the right flank of the enemy and continued the forward movement. While our Confederate troops were assaulting the main force of the enemy in the breastworks, Captain Nelms was attacking them on the flank and rear. The enemy soon gave way and broke, hastily leaving the breastworks and rushing pell-mell in the direction of General Grant's main body of troops.

This battle relieved the situation that was threatening some of the Confederate supplies at Beaver Dam Station. In this fight the Confederates lost many good and true soldiers.

The 11th Mississippi was among the troops that had been

detached and put under temporary command of Gen. Jubal Early. When we moved back to the vicinity of Spottsylvania Courthouse, each brigade joined its respective division. The next day, May 11th, was spent in skirmishing and maneuvering for advantage in a defensive position, with considerable fighting at times during the day. Preparations had been made for an expected struggle the next day. On the morning of the 12th the enemy made a heavy attack on Early's front and broke the line where it was occupied by Johnston's Division.

At this time and place a scene occurred of which Mississippians are justly proud. One of General Lee's staff officers states that on receipt of a message from General Rodes for more troops, he was sent by General Lee to bring Harris's Mississippi Brigade from the extreme right. General Lee met the brigade and rode at its head until it came under fire and a round shot passed so near the general that the soldiers entreated him to go back. Lee turned to the troops and said, "If you will promise me to drive those people from our works I will go back," the brigade shouted its promise, and the staff officer says:

"As the column of Mississippians came out at a double-quick, an aide-de-camp came up to General Rodes with a message from General Ramseur that he could hold out only a few minutes longer unless help was at hand. Harris's Brigade was thrown instantly into the fight, the column being formed into line under a tremendous fire and on very difficult ground. Never did a brigade go into the fire of battle under greater trials; never did a brigade do its duty more nobly.

Heth's Division occupied a position to the right of where Johnston had been assaulted, and Harris's Mississippi Brigade made such a desperate fight. The enemy made an advance on General Heth's front under cover of a pine thicket within seventy-five yards of the position occupied by the 11th Mississippi. When they promptly opened fire on our lines they were quickly repulsed. After this fire fight, one hundred and fifty picked men from Davis's Mississippi Brigade were thrown forward as sharpshooters and skirmishers, and Captain W. G. Nelms, commander of Company G, 11th Mississippi Regiment, was once again sent for by Brigadier General Davis to take charge of this detail and deploy the skirmishers in front of our brigade. Since most of the Prairie Guards were sharpshooters we were called on again. Our detail had no protection, except the undergrowth of small pines and other growths, and occasionally an oak tree. We skirmishers were in close proximity to a heavy line of battle that was

Confederate sharpshooter

keeping up a continual musket fire all the time.

Captain Nelms had to supervise the whole line, the full length of the brigade. Necessarily he had to go from one end of the line to the other frequently, while the men under him were being continually killed and wounded, and had to make frequent requests for reinforcements as his men disappeared from casualties. Our unit was chopped to pieces and our total losses including killed and wounded on that skirmish line that day were one hundred and twenty men. It has always been a mystery how our commander of that little squad escaped that day, having been under a continuous fire of the enemy all day with no protection at all.

At one time during the day when one of the frequent details was made to fill the depleted ranks in the skirmish line, a private named Adison Burney, a gallant young man, was one of the detail. When detailed he remarked that no man could get to that line alive, the musket firing from the enemy was such, but he said, "I have been ordered and I will go." He was mortally wounded before he reached the line. When night came the conflict ceased. Things were comparatively quiet for the next few days, except picket firing and conflicts occasionally with flanking parties.

On the 18th another assault was made upon our lines, but it produced no impression. On the 20th of May, after twelve days of skirmish and battles at Spottsylvania against a superior force, General Lee's information led him to believe that the enemy was about to attempt another flank movement and interpose his army between the Confederate capitol and its defenders. To defeat this purpose Longstreet was ordered to move at midnight in the direction of Hanover Junction, and on the following day Ewell's and Hill's Corps marched for the same point.

The attack by Union Generals Wright and Hancock, planned for first light to catch the Confederate army off guard, was slow in getting started. Hours were lost while the advancing infantry cautiously occupied the original Confederate position at the Bloody Angle, then moved on to the second line of defense the Confederates had constructed in the Mule Shoe sector of the trenches on May 12. There the Federals encountered, not a thin grey line like Grant anticipated, but Richard Ewell's stubborn veterans supported by twenty nine pieces of artillery. Around eight a.m. the Confederate gunners could see the Federals in the abandoned works like fish in a barrel and gleefully began shooting. Our brigade, the 11th Mississippi, held part of the line during the last Union assault near the Spottsylvania Courthouse. The Federals lost approximately 2,000 men.

In the battle of the 12th we were sheltered by strong breastworks and we suffered very little although my brother, Charlie F. Wilkins, was wounded. The next day the Battle of the Po River was fought, in which Colonel Green of the 11th Mississippi was killed and T. S. Scales of our Company was wounded. James R. Montgomery, Company A, the University Greys of the 11th Mississippi, who was mortally wounded at Spottsylvania, used the last of his strength to write this poignant letter to his father, A. V. Montgomery of

161

SPOTTSYLVANIA COURTHOUSE

Camden, in Madison County, Mississippi. As his hand grew shaky and as his blood stained the page, he wrote:

"Dear Father,

This is my last letter to you. I went into battle this evening as courier for Gen'l Heth. I have been struck by a piece of shell and my right shoulder is horribly mangled and I know death is inevitable. I am very weak but I write to you because I know you would be delighted to read a word from your dying son. I know death is near, that I will die far from home and friends and of my early youth, but I have friends here, too, who are kind to me. My friend, Fairfax, will write you at my request and give you the particulars of my death. My grave will be marked so that you may visit it if you so desire to do so, but is optional with you, whether you let my remains rest here or in Miss. I would like to rest in the grave yard with my dear mother and brothers but it's a matter of minor importance. Let us all try to reunite in heaven. I pray my God to forgive my sins and I feel that his promises are such that he will forgive me and save me. Give my love to all my friends. My strength now fails me. My horse and my equipments will be left for you. Again, a long farewell to you, may we meet in heaven.

Your dying son,
J. R. Montgomery."

North and South Anna

CHAPTER XIV

The next engagement in which we participated was that of the North Anna on May 24th. The critical moment had arrived; now was the time for Lee to strike a damaging blow against an isolated quarter of Grant's army. This movement was so important that Lee believed only he could coordinate it with the implacable resolution it required. None of his three corps commanders was taken into his confidence, as Lee found himself unable to trust any of them to carry out the assault.

The ailing A. P. Hill's failure to move decisively against Union General Warren had eliminated him from consideration; Dick Anderson was too inexperienced and Richard Ewell in too fragile a state of health to bear the stress. It was up to Lee to direct the eruption of two Confederate corps from their carefully prepared positions to crush Hancock's corps. According to his aide Charles Venable, "Lee would gladly have compelled battle in his position there. He was anxious now to strike a telling blow, as he was convinced that General Grant's men were dispirited by the bloody repulses of their repeated attacks on our lines."

But attack orders were never issued. At this vital moment, Lee's body betrayed him. "In the midst of these operations on the North Anna," reported Venable, "General Lee was taken sick and confined to his tent. As he lay prostrated by his sickness, he would often repeat, 'We must strike them a blow - we must never let them pass us again, we must strike them a blow.'"

In a private agony he shared with no one, the Confederate commander realized that the chance for victory that he had been seeking for three weeks was slipping from his grasp.

Brief, violent combat erupted at two points as groping Union forces stumbled through passing rain showers and into Lee's trap.

Pushing eastward after crossing the North Anna upstream from Ox Ford, one of Burnside's brigades moved against some virtually impregnable entrenchments held by A. P. Hill's corps. The unauthorized Federal attack was directed by Brig. Gen. James H. Ledlie, a man who owed his rise in the ranks to political pull rather than ability. And this day he owed his bellicosity to what one Massachusetts soldier described as "that artificial courage known throughout the Yankee army as 'Dutch courage'. We Rebels called it "pop skull courage."

Advancing without supports, Ledlie's men charged into a rainstorm and a storm of lead. The wavering Federal line was shattered by a Confederate counterattack, and "Every man became his own general," as one officer admitted afterward.

Ledlie, who had quickly lost all control over events, let his men fall back toward Quarles Mill, where the rest of the division had dug itself in. Lt. Col. Stephen Weld of the 56th Massachusetts wrote in his diary this assessment of the whole affair: "General Ledlie made a botch of it. Had too much booze on board, I think."

Although more than two hundred Federals were killed, wounded, or missing thanks to Ledlie's action, his immediate superior, Gen. Ambrose Burnside, backed his division commander, stating officially that "he and his men had behaved gallantly", and there the matter ended.

Even as Ledlie's men were advancing, Thomas Smyth's brigade was caught up in a fierce firefight a mile or so south of the North Anna, along the R. F. & P. Railroad line.

Before long, John Gibbon's entire division was involved in a stubborn engagement with Ewell's corps, which crackled through a sudden thunderstorm and lasted well into the night before ending inconclusively.

At last Grant sensed the danger. He was still not certain what Lee was doing, but it was clear to him that his opponent had not fallen back behind the South Anna River. In an 8:20 P.M. message to Burnside, Grant confessed that the "situation of the enemy . . . (was) different from what I expected." The optimistic marching orders for May 25 were changed. Hancock was to entrench his position; Burnside was to halt the passage of his wagon train to the south bank of the North Anna and hold the connection between Warren and Hancock. Warren would probe forward at daylight and fix the Confederate position while Wright protected his right and rear.

Grant also decided to end the unwieldy dual-command structure that had maintained Burnside's Ninth Corps as an independent force. Under Special Order Number 25, the corps was made a part of the Army of the Potomac. Now Burnside would report directly to Meade. "It was found," noted Horace Porter, "that such a consideration would be much better for purposes of administration, and give more unity to the movements."

Bethesda Church
Chapter XV

On June 2nd, under the command of General Early, Heth's division fought the Battle of Bethesda Church.

At dawn on Monday, May 30th our boys shook the dew from their blankets, chewed a hasty morning meal of hoe cakes and salt pork and fell into marching order.

From his headquarters in the Clarke family house, near Atlee's Station, Robert E. Lee looked for an opportunity to throw a wrench into the smoothly turning wheels of Grant's juggernaut.

Lee had positioned our army carefully to counter any Union moves west or south. For the moment it was wait and see. Lee's actions this day would depend upon Grant's.

Union Gen. Charles Griffin's division led the way for the Fifth Corps. At daylight, skirmishers from the 22nd Massachusetts filed out first in a thin line of one rank, with the men five paces apart. I shall never forget our march through Totopotomoy wood, keeping in line, over briers and fallen trees and stumps," recalled Henry B. James of the 32nd Massachusetts. This "new ground" slowed Union Gen. Charles Griffin's advance to a crawl.

Pushing southward across the Totopotomoy, Griffin's Union battle line swung westward on the Shady Grove Church Road. Flankers spread the line out even further and kept contact with the Old Church Road, which paralleled their route, about a mile to the south. This east-west thoroughfare led eventually to Mechanicsville, near Richmond, and was also called the Mechanicsville Pike. As the blue columns came to cross the Totopotomoy lowlands, scattered but obstinate resistance forced the Federals to deploy into lines of battle that struggled through the brambly swampland bordering the creek.

Further to the north, Hancock's Second Corps was also pushing westward, with Wright's Sixth and Burnside's Ninth in close support.

By the time the sun was approaching its midday position, Robert E. Lee had a good picture of what was going on and a clear idea what it all meant. Two Yankee corps had crossed to the south of Totopotomoy Creek and were taking up positions on the near bank, facing west. At 11:00 A.M., the grey-haired commander explained things in a dispatch to Gen. Richard Anderson: "After fortifying this line they will

Jubal A. Early

probably make another move by their left flank over towards the Chickahominy. This is just a repetition of their former movements." Lee also saw opportunity beckoning. "This movement can only be arrested by striking at once at that part of their force which has crossed the Topotomoy in General Early's front. I have desired him to do this if he thought it could be done advantageously."

TITHES OF BLOOD

Our commander Jubal Early **did** think it could be done advantageously. Anticipating having to follow the Yankees' next crab-like shift to the south, Early had our men cut cross-country traces from their Shady Grove Church Road lines down to the Old Church Road. The cavalry reports indicated that the left flank of the Yankee thrust along the first of these roads only lightly brushed the second. That Union flank was ripe for turning, Early argued, and Lee agreed. By early afternoon the acting corps commander had assembled his strike force. Spearheaded by Robert Rodes's division, it was poised to sweep eastward along the Old Church Road, with Bethesda Church as its goal. Once that was secured, Early's men would be able to swing northward to slice in behind the forward elements of the Yankee Fifth Corps.

Something of Lee's thinking can be gleaned from his admonition to Gen. Richard Anderson later in the day: "Do everything for the grand object, the destruction of the enemy."

Early brought our corps past the left flank of Charles Griffin's division, which was spread across the Shady Grove Church Road. The 22nd Massachusetts, still scouting in front of Griffin, spotted what was happening. "Several times our skirmishers, when halting for a few moments in the openings in the woods, could see Early's heavy columns in the distance, moving to our left," recalled one Bay State soldier.

Rodes's division formed at right angles to the Old Church Road and began a spirited advance eastward. We had not gone far before we came across the enemy in the form of Hardin's brigade of the Pennsylvania Reserves. They were posted in a slender breastworks. We charged them fiercely and they fled in . . . confusion." It was a little past 2:00 P.M.

Hardin's First Brigade was steamrollered. Hardin later described it: "(Rodes's) column, five or six times the strength of the First Brigade, came down the Mechanicsville Pike at a run, its left resting on the pike, and its front extended off to the right. . . . The volley or two delivered by our feeble force made no impression on the enemy; they ran over and around us. . . . , and his division headquarters arrived amidst the headquarters of the First Brigade before the latter could extricate itself. Our troops were so confident

Route steps

of his ultimate success that we did not stop to secure the First Brigade prisoners, but continued to charge on down the pike."

Rodes's battle lines smashed into Crawford's two remaining brigades near Bethesda Church. "We were attacked on both flanks with great fury," one dazed Pennsylvania prisoner reported. Charles Wainwright, the Fifth Corps artillery chief, figured that Hardin's line held for perhaps five minutes, and the two brigade lines near the church for a little longer, before the Yankee line broke and skedaddled to the north. In Union

TITHES OF BLOOD

Colonel Wainwright's opinion, Crawford's men "were rather indiscriminately hurrying back to the Shady Grove Road." Some regiments fell apart completely.

It was enlivening to our boys to witness the confusion as the Yankee troops tried to get over some marshy ground. When they reached the swamp, the most available places for crossing were crowded and jammed with men. We Rebels had advanced rapidly in pursuit, and were sending a shower of bullets into the struggling mass in the swamp. . . . one Yankee soldier jumped for what he believed to be a firm spot of ground, but it proved to be anything but solid, for he sank into the mire almost to his knees. . . . he . . . lost considerable time in extricating himself from the mire; and . . . by blocking his retreat route I took him prisoner.

All of us Confederate attackers were so keyed up that many of the boys pushed past the Yankees and went on to Bethesda Church. We were actually moving in the wrong direction, to wit, parallel to the Union lines. Then Early ordered his old division, now commanded by Stephen Ramseur, to come forward, and at the same time requested the First Corps commander,

Stephen Dodson Ramseur

171

BETHESDA CHURCH

Richard Anderson, "to advance a division along the road to Old Church and take the enemy in the flank." Early's plan seemed to be to build up a strong line at right angles to the Union advance and roll the whole thing up all the way to the Pamunkey. Communication with Anderson was erratic, however, and the requested support did not materialize. Early had his men in position but was uncertain what to do until Stephen Ramseur took a hand in the matter.

Early was surveying the distant Union position as Ramseur brought his division up, with John Pegram's brigade - now commanded by a popular Georgia colonel named Edward Willis - in the van. The combative, high-strung General Ramseur was consumed with impatience to attack. Lt. Col. Charles B. Christian was standing near the head of Pegram's column when it came under fire from a lone Yankee cannon, posted well in front of the main enemy line. Christian remembered hearing Ramseur say to Early, "General, let me take that gun. . . ." According to Christian, "General Early vigorously advised and protested against it. Ramseur insisted, General Early finally acquiesced in the move."

Our boys charged and were met by a hail of cannon and rifle balls although we could not see a single Yankee. Our line melted away as if by magic - every brigade, staff and field officer was cut down, (mostly killed outright) in an incredibly short time.

We crossed that field of carnage and mounted the parapet of the enemy's works and poured a volley in their faces. They gave way, but two lines of battle, close in their rear, rose and

172

each delivered a volley into our ranks in rapid succession. . . . Our line, already decimated, was now almost annihilated.

The attack was over. As Jubal Early would report this evening, "The enemy was found in heavy force, entrenched. . . . Pegram's brigade was compelled to retire, sustaining considerable loss.

In the Confederate ranks, the pain of loss was mixed with hot anger. Lt. Colonel Christian, wounded and captured in the engagement, remembered it as "the bloodiest fight of our Civil War, considering the number engaged on each side. . . . The loss of officers was full ninety per cent of all engaged." Among them were the dashing Colonel Edward Willis and his aide, "the chivalrous young Lt. Joseph Randolph, of Richmond." The mortally wounded Willis passed away on May 31, using his last breath to declare, "I am no more afraid to die than I was to go into the battle."

A lot of our boys blamed the impetuous Stephen Ramseur, eager to prove himself in his first outing as a division commander. "A murder for ambition's sake," was how one soldier diarist put it. "Ramseur was to blame for the whole thing and ought to have been shot for the part he played in it," one of his own officers declared. Ole Jube turned a blind eye to the matter, not even mentioning Ramseur's name in his report of the action. Ramseur himself engaged in no self-recrimination. His letters termed the combat at Bethesda Church a "hard fight" and contained no hint of guilt. It was a hard fight all right, our guts - his glory!

Confederate and Federal losses in the fighting around

BETHESDA CHURCH

Bethesda Church and the Totopotomoy were "light" when compared with those from the wilderness and Spottsylvania. The cost to Lee's army, based on a current re-examination of Confederate casualty data, is now estimated at: killed and wounded, 811; captured, 348; total, 1,159. Grant's losses have been put at: killed and wounded, 679; captured, 52; total, 731.

The 11th Mississippi Regiment suffered considerable loss and Dennis O'Sullivan of Company E lost a leg and died shortly thereafter in Chimborazo Hospital in Richmond.

Cold Harbor

Chapter XVI

After several days of skirmishing and maneuvering, on the 3rd of June the two armies were brought face to face at Cold Harbor. General Grant made fruitless efforts to pursue and drive back our forces under General Lee. Our troops were protected by temporary earthworks and while under cover of these we were assaulted by the enemy.

At four thirty A.M., on June 3, 1864, bugles sounded the advance. Along two miles of line, more than 50,000 Union infantrymen of the II, VI and XVIII corps began clambering out of their works and charging toward our formidable fortifications, still wreathed in morning mists, several hundred yards away. When the Federals closed within musket range, we Confederates behind the breastworks raised up deliberately, rested our rifles upon the parapet, and fired volley after volley into the rushing but disorganized ranks of the enemy. The first line reeled and attempted to flee the field, but were met by the next column, which halted the retreating troops with their bayonets, our gun butts and officers' swords, until the greater number were turned to the second assault. Our boys then poured a galling fire into the tangled mass of advancing and retreating troops. The fire from a nearby Confederate battery was so intense that at every discharge we saw "heads, arms, legs, guns flying high in the air.

In front of our brigade, one Federal regiment simply

COLD HARBOR

melted away - save for its colorbearer, who, unaware that there was no longer anyone behind him, steadily advanced with the flag. "Go back! Go back! We'll kill you!" some of our boys shouted. But still the Union soldier came on. When he got close enough, a few of us even stood up and waved him away. He finally stopped, and taking the staff from its socket, rested it on the ground. He then deliberately looked, first to the right rear, and then his left rear, and then seemingly for the first time taking in the situation, with the same moderation gathered in the flag, right-shoulder-shifted his flag-staff, came to an about face as deliberately, and walked back amid the cheers of our men, who never saw anything equal to such bravery before or since.

But the charge was in vain; the assault was repulsed along the whole line, and the loss on the Federal side was fearful. The ground in front, over which the enemy charged, was literally covered with their dead and wounded. When the command was given to renew the assault, the Federal soldiers sullenly and silently declined. The order was issued through the officers to their subordinate commanders and from them descended through the combat commands, but no man stirred, and the immobile lines pronounced a verdict, silent yet emphatic, against further slaughter. The loss on the Union side in this action was over 7,000, while we lost 1,500.

Petersburg
Chapter XVII

After the Battle of Cold Harbor we rested and refitted for several weeks. On June 12th we crossed the James River on a pontoon bridge below Chafin's Farm and proceeded on to Petersburg. We immediately relieved some troops who had already been in the trenches for some time. Ironically enough, our position was directly above the exact spot where Grant would spring his famous mine on July 30th. We remained in this entrenched position for several weeks, when providentially, we were relieved and held in reserve several miles behind the front near the city limits of Petersburg. We badly needed this respite as we had been marching and fighting for a very long time.

After the first week of rest, we were called to arms and marched up toward Richmond to meet a threat posed by the Yankee II Corps but this problem never materialized so we were immediately marched back down to our Petersburg reserve camp.

On July 30th at 4:45 on a hot still morning G. B. Triplett, C. S. Cooper, my cousin James Norwood and myself were whispering silently to each other to keep from going to sleep while we carried out company guard duty. I raised my hand to swat a pesky mosquito when all of a sudden the ground commenced to shake like an earthquake. Then we heard a long, deep rumble way down deep in the earth. Then a great upward bulge occurred in our line of trenches right where we had manned the line a short while ago. The huge, round column of earth now rose straight up like a picture of that Italian volcano, Vesuvius, I once saw in Papa's Matte-Brun's Geography book.

The whole dang thing blew apart with a huge spout of flame and a crack of noise that broke windows behind us in Petersburg and then the sky was full of a continuous roaring sound like a mighty thunderstorm. Directly the sky was full of logs, caissons, horses, cannons and, worst of all, human bodies looking like little rag dolls tossed end over end high in the seething air.

Our guard detail stood trembling in stunned silence. "It's an earthquake!" yelled C. S. Cooper. "It's a volcano!" screamed G. B. Triplett. "It's the end of the world and I ain't

The Battle of the Crater

repented yet!" wailed my cousin James Norwood. I just stood there stunned.

We definitely did not have to wake up the camp! The whole company was running around like a chicken with his head cut off. Pretty soon a staff officer thundered up from General Heth's headquarters and we were soon on the march for that cauldron of hell forever known as Grant's Crater. By the time we arrived, Gen. "Little Billy" Mahone's boys had whipped most of the Yankee attack party and run them back to their own lines with the help of their commander, the Yankee General Ledlie, who, per usual, was drunk back in his bomb-proof bunker. I wished we faced more Union generals like that. The Yanks lost 4,500 men to our 1,500.

After the battle of the crater finally ceased, we were ordered to occupy a line of trenches near the crater.

The first morning after we occupied the trenches, I was sitting on the ground conversing with Captain Ervin and finding out the news that he had received from Noxubee County, when suddenly I was jerked to my feet by what seemed to me to be the loudest explosion I had ever heard. The concussion deafened me for some time and gave me a violent headache. I shortly found out that this explosion was caused by the firing of our own cannon, a 150-pounder Armstrong siege rifle! Compared to the 12-pounder Napoleons we were used to, you can imagine our shock. We soon learned that the only way you can counter a siege-gun's concussion is to stand on tiptoe and open your mouth. Even though we took this precaution, the report was bad on our nerves.

The trench warfare was just awful. The summer heat was intense, the dust billowed in stifling clouds and the mosquitoes and black flies were unbearable. Our rations were just as vile. We were issued spoiled meat, moldy bacon, and weevil infested peas and cornmeal.

Night and day the firing was kept up. At night, the mortars threw shells and the light was as beautiful as any fireworks and then the blaze of fire from the line of musketry would begin at one point and travel the whole length of the

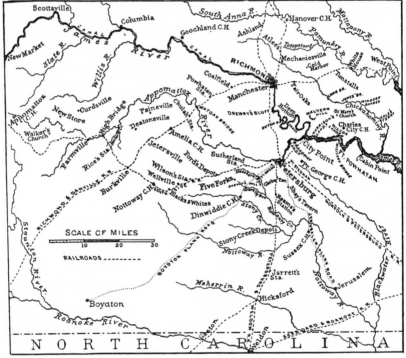

Petersburg and Weldon Railroad

line and make the scene a veritable hell on earth. When there was a lull in the firing, the men would drop down into the blood and excrement filled trenches and fall into exhausted sleep. Our Petersburg trenches and the Yankee trenches paralleling ours were usually only 200 yards or less apart so you had to be very careful not to expose yourself to Yankee fire. It was a nightmarish existence, living and sleeping in that dirty ditch day in and day out.

After two weeks of this torture, we were glad to be ordered out of the trenches of Petersburg for some open ground fighting down on the Weldon Railroad.

On August 17th, Union General Warren's V Corps marched three miles to the west and occupied more than a mile of our railroad track near Globe Tavern. The Yankees then began moving north along the tracks toward Petersburg. They had to be stopped. A. P. Hill immediately pulled Heth's Division out of reserve and we were soon on the double quick march to meet this latest threat.

The llth Mississippi was on the point of this attack on the 18th. Our brave Captain E. A. Ervin led the charge with his sword pointed toward the enemy. Since he was out front of our battle line, he made a perfect target for the Yankees. We hadn't charged more than fifty yards before he was hit. The force of the bullet impact spun him around twice before he hit the ground, his sword clattering on the rocky soil. One of the "line closers" who followed us picked him and his sword up and took him to the aid station. Thank God, his wound wasn't critical. Later on, however, we learned that

PETERSBURG

Reuben Scales was captured.

Our charge continued with the high pitched scream of the Rebel Yell and our battle flags flying. We easily drove the Federals back and advanced several hundred yards. When we stopped for a "blow", however, the Yankees counterattacked but we stood and delivered two well aimed volleys and the Yanks fell in windrows before our massed fire. The Yanks then skedaddled and a lull came over the field of battle. The quiet was shortly broken by a huge cheer and I looked around to find the cause. Riding up behind us was the finest sight I ever saw: Gen. Robert Lee and our corps commander, Gen. A. P. Hill, were riding in to meet our Division commander, Gen. Henry Heth, for a council of war. General Lee was riding bolt upright in the saddle on his lovely dappled grey horse, Traveler. Just the mere sight of him, so handsome and fine, was like a great bolt of energy to our weary boys and we would gladly have charged the Blue Bellies again if he had ordered us to do so.

Gen. A. P. Hill also looked impressive that day. He rode up with a firm and graceful seat and looked every inch a soldier in his legendary slouch hat, round jacket and long yellow gauntlets. He was small but built like an athlete. His expression today was grave but gentle and his high flushed cheekbones accented his bright flashing blue eyes. He looked like a banty rooster on the prod.

The generals were so close that I could hear General Hill's sharp, metallic voice as he discussed the immediate situation with General Heth. General Lee then waved his hand toward the north and said to Hill, "General, I think if you will send a force through those woods and strike those people on their flank, you will find that flank in the air. At the same time that this force attacks, let General Heth attack as he did today."

The generals then ordered up Maj. Gen. William Mahone's division and Willie Peagram's artillery to reinforce us. Mahone looked more like a leprechaun than a field general but he was a canny tactician and a fierce leader. Willie Peagram looked like a myopic school boy but he was the top artillery colonel in the ANV. The attack was delayed until the next day, August 19th. A hard rain started about noon but at four that afternoon, yelling like banshees, we struck the Union left flank which, just as General Lee had predicted, was indeed "in the air". We bounded forward and swept over all obstructions, pressing the Yankees back with heavy loss. We carried two Yankee positions while firing less than 1,000 shots and we captured 1,800 Yanks. We re-formed and waited and, while we waited, the Yankees reinforced. When General Hill ordered us to attack at dusk our attack failed. We were tremendously out-numbered by mostly fresh Union troops.

We were soon relieved and marched back toward Petersburg for a short, well-deserved rest.

On the 21st of August we were again ordered to march out to defend the Weldon Railroad. It was a stormy Sunday and General Hill had called on us once more to try to break the Yankee lines. We were "stove-up", foot sore and as

William Mahone   *William Johnson Pegram*

bedraggled as a dying calf in a thunder storm but we still believed in our cause and obeyed orders. We were marched up behind Willie Peagram's battery which was bombarding Warren's earthworks four hundred yards across the way.

The cannon crews were hatless, stripped to the waist and they were covered with splotches of black powder and blood. They worked like madmen with rammer and powder, projectile and lanyard. With bruised shoulders and bloody hands against the wheels, they heaved the heavy guns back into their places after each recoil. There were no audible commands in that awful environment of buzzing canister and exploding shells; only little Willie Peagram, the top commander, flitting here and there, to re-sight a gun or lend encouragement. He was among Lee's chosen few.

We were positioned directly behind the Davis house. Soon our division batteries arrived and General Heth also rode up and began placing the batteries. I heard him yell to his orderly, "Is there anybody still in that house?" Without waiting for an answer, the general ran into the house and soon emerged with a lovely girl of about eighteen. I could see the general yelling at her to run but she just stood there with arms akimbo. "I will die here before I would run!" she yelled back. She stood there fully a minute, shaking her delicate fist at the Yankee batteries and then deliberately walked off in the direction the general had indicated. Right then a Yankee shell hit the Davis house and then the pine trees all around our position. Shrapnel was screaming all around us as we hugged the ground.

General Heth ran back to General Stone. "Charge those batteries," he ordered. We quickly lined up and charged forward. Our artillery kept up a covering barrage until we were up on the parapet. I remember seeing that lovely old battle flag leading me up when I was suddenly spun around, a searing pain shot through my thigh and the world exploded. I was back at Sunnyside in Noxubee County with all my family, including Henry and Davy, eating country ham, peas and corn bread and skillet-fried squash washed down with home-churned buttermilk . . . . that vision dimmed and I saw sobbing rain clouds overhead. Then a grizzled face topped with a blue forage cap hazily filled my contorted view. "War's over for you, Reb." I heard him say. Then the great pain hit again and the storm-blurred world whirled away.

Epilogue
Noxubee Memories

The rooster crowed, the jackass brayed and old snaps, the pointer, bumped his rheumatoid backbone on the undercarriage of the creaking country house. It was a golden dawn in Noxubee County, Mississippi. The early-morning light refracted through the greying lead-glass panes, and now darkly through the misty memory of a grown man, then a tousled-headed town boy with a chunk of joy in his throat and the world before him.

I pulled on my clothes and made my way through the rambling, labyrinthine country house, out the never-locked back door, and onto the tin-roofed walkway to the old kitchen, which stood ten yards out back. I shivered in the morning cold until I pushed open the weather-beaten kitchen door. The heat inside warmed my body as well as my spirit. Granky, my Wilkins grandmother, held sway over a great wood stove, and her sons, recently spared from the Axis hordes, swilled great cups of strong coffee from ancient stoneware mugs. That smell of hickory smoke, coffee and thick slabs of home-cured bacon is still fresh after all these years.

Once an old Eskimo woman, sick and depressed in a far and strange land, told her nurse, "Sometimes I raise my hands before my eyes and stare at them; right in my own hands I can see the shorelines, beaches, lakes and mountains

EPILOGUE

where I came from." In my heart's eye, when I see Granky's hands - plump, white, dishwater hands - kneading the biscuit dough, I remember where I came from. Those hands were once artist's hands at Mississippi State College for Women so very long ago, but she had given up art for a loftier and higher form of sculpture: kneading love into the dough.

The menfolk made plans for the day's hunt over an incredibly fine breakfast of grits, scrambled eggs, thick slabs of bacon, cat-head biscuits and homemade fig preserves from the old fig tree behind the smokehouse. Thank goodness no one had yet discovered cholesterol, triglycerides or carcinogens! We were in the best of times. Granky's boys were safe, and the world had a vibrancy and brilliance that only children can really feel.

The guineas were just starting their raucous cackling when Grandaddy Tyson Wilkins took me in tow. He and I would hunt the Back Forty. Old liver-marked Snaps ran by the smokehouse and headed out to "Quail country". Grandaddy slipped three shells into his old beat-up Browning Sweet Sixteen, and we moved out past squealing pigs, pump house, horse barn, rusting harrows, and other extraneous refuse that always surrounds an old country homestead. The sun was just up and a thin fog still blanketed the gently rolling prairie hills. "Hup, Snaps!" Grandaddy called. The old pointer slowed and started to work, ranging back and forth, a flicker of white in and out of the patches of ground fog in the surreal early morning landscape. Then the white dot was stationary.

TITHES OF BLOOD

"He's got 'em!" whispered Grandaddy as I ran after him, panting and expectant, but not really knowing quite what to expect. He handed me the shotgun and whispered, "Shoot a bird, not the covey." I have never felt such responsibility except the time a nurse handed me a little bloody, squalling miracle named Scott and in that awesome moment I saw God."

Snaps had worked in tight on the covey in a perfect point. My heart was in overdrive. The sage crunched underfoot while I found the safety. "Walk past 'im," whispered Grandaddy.

An explosion occurred, and the buff bombshells rocketed out of the sage. I swung on the whole covey. Gun blast, kick, and no bird fell. I forgot to shoot again.

"We'll get the singles," promised Grandaddy. He then showed me how; with the pointer holding pretty, a single thundered up from underfoot, to explode in a shower of feathers. Old Snaps dutifully brought back each one, mouthing them gently, and we soon had six birds. Grandaddy called a rest break about noon.

We stopped at an old falling-down dogtrot house. The old man pulled a couple of roast beef sandwiches out of his hunting coat. "I'm feeling my seventy-four years," he confessed. "Let's sit here on the porch, and while we're here, I guess this is as good a time as any to tell you what tired really is and what courage is all about.

"My daddy, your great-grandaddy, had this farm and left me the big house. Some day in school, you'll learn in the

189

history books about Gen. Robert E. Lee and the Army of Northern Virginia. I don't know everything there is to know about all the battles, but I do know that Daddy was in our local company, the Prairie Guards, Company E of the 11th Mississippi Regiment in Lee's army. They were one of the first companies to volunteer, and since General Grant wasn't even a general then, much less raising havoc in Mississippi, Daddy's regiment was shipped to Virginia and fought under Lee for the whole war.

He went through every battle that Lee fought, and was wounded seven times. It takes a heap of courage and a lot of love for your homeland to keep going when you're hurt, tired, sick, hungry and thirsty most of the time. Both of his brothers, Henry Martin Wilkins and Davy Crockett Wilkins, were killed, one on either side of him, when they went up the hill in Pickett's Charge at Gettysburg. Out of the thirty-seven men in their company, only one man was able to answer roll call back down at the bottom of Cemetery Ridge that evening. Only one man, boy! I know folks in almost every house around here that grieved for a lost boy or two.

"Son, all day you've been complaining, tired, thirsty or something. I want you to remember what I just told you. In spite of thirst, exhaustion and other infirmities, those simple country boys still went up that hill regardless of politics or ideology. They were defending what they perceived was right, protecting their homes and families and they persevered through untold suffering.

"Right after Gettysburg, Daddy fought all the way back to Hatcher's Run right before Appomattox. By then, our

190

troops were pitiful skeleton boys with no shoes and tattered, threadbare uniforms. They were starving and sick, but they still had that bright glint of bravery and total, even mystical, commitment in their eyes.

"On the last night, they were completely surrounded by the Yankees and Lee's army was pushed up against a creek called Hatcher's Run. Just as the sun was setting for the last time on the greatest army the world has ever known, a long, shrill, rolling, cry welled up. Starting three miles up Hatcher's Run and rolling down the Confederate lines, the Rebel Yell rolled like thunder down that creek, telling the Yankees that we might be destroyed but our indomitable spirit would never be defeated.

"The next day, that bunch of pitiful scarecrow-boys was thrown into line. Our bloody and tattered Confederate battle flag still boldly fluttered before each regiment, only a few yards apart because each one had been decimated down to mere company size. General Lee and General Gordon rode the line, tears flowing down their cheeks. They knew the end was near, not just for the army, but for a way of life.

"Gen. John B. Gordon stopped his prancing bay in front of a pitiful Confederate soldier. Both of his arms had been almost shot away, and they dangled helplessly at his sides. 'Get to the aid station, sir,' the general ordered. 'You cannot go into combat in your condition.'

"I know I can't fight, sir,' the soldier replied, 'but I can still yell!'"

"'I CAN STILL YELL!'"

EPILOGUE

Lord, how I remembered that story. When the path grows dim, when the trail gets too rough, when the world closes in, I think of that pitiful, starving boy in homespun grey with the glint in his steel-blue eyes and a love that transcends all understanding in his heart.

Grandaddy pulled out an old, yellowed clipping from his pocket and handed it to me. "I thought you would like to have your great-grandaddy's eulogy, which was written by his commanding officer, Captain A. J. Ervin."

I started to read:

Eulogy of Thomas J. Wilkins, Co. E, 11th Mississippi Regiment by Captain A J. Ervin:

The subject of this sketch was raised in Noxubee County, Mississippi, and died on the 8th day of January, 1920, having lived about eighty-two years.

He heard the call of his State and Southland in '61, and became a member of the Prairie Guards, an infantry company organized at Crawford, Mississippi which afterwards became Company E, 11th Mississippi Regiment. The regiment was ordered to Harpers Ferry, Virginia, in May of that year, and served the entire four years thereafter in the army of Northern Virginia. There were four brothers of his family in the company.

In reviewing an old muster roll which I possessed, and which I have kept a record of each member's service I find this fact: That the blood of a Wilkins enriched the soil of every general battle-field in either Virginia, Maryland or Pennsylvania, with but few exceptions. Two of his brothers,

TITHES OF BLOOD

Henry and Dave, made the "supreme sacrifice" with Pickett in his heroic charge upon Cemetery Heights, and they sleep in an unknown grave where they fell at Gettysburg. Another brother, Charley, was wounded several times, but served throughout the war, and lived many years afterwards within a few miles of his boyhood home, dying a few years since.

The subject of this sketch was wounded more than once, the last time on the 6th of May in the Battle of the Wilderness, a day which will always be remembered as the crowning glory of Lee's army in its gallant and supreme heroic and successful effort to stop and defeat the Federal army of more than five times our number, and commanded by their favorite and most successful general, U. S. Grant. I was closely associated with him in this trying period of the war, and as commander of his company for the last two years of the war, I think I can speak advisedly of him as a man and a soldier. He was gallant and dependable in battle, and in camp and on the march he was always joyous and happy; never a cloud, however threatening, but that he could see the sunshine beyond. His most marked characteristic, however, was his intense and active interest in a sick or suffering comrade. No march could be so disagreeable and so protracted; no weather so severe as to prohibit his spending the night in a vigil by the pallet of a sick or suffering comrade; and he was one of the few who seemed to enjoy in battling with death - in comforting where he could not cure; in soothing where he could not save.

EPILOGUE

After the bloody tragedy, closed when the Stars and Bars were folded, and grounded in gloom, in sorrow, and in tears at Appomattox, he returned home and boldly took up the duties of citizenship and lived a long and successful life; a full, round life; a devoted husband, a kind and loving father, and a true and faithful friend. As a comrade in arms; as an associate in peace, I gladly pay this feeble tribute to his memory. I deem it not amiss or inappropriate, to say to his boys and family, that his life, my life, human life is continuous; it is not bounded by the few years of our activities here, neither is it limited by the short span of time between our cradles and our graves, but it extends from our cradles to the farthest stretches of eternity, so that being a fact, we poor mortal pilgrims here on earth, by faith in God, by keeping His statutes, by walking in His footsteps, and by His grace, can look forward to that life beyond the now, where every pain, every sorrow, will be lifted from our hearts, every tear wiped from every eye, where we can clasp again the hands which have long been hidden, and hear again and be thrilled by the sweet voices which have long been silent; where meeting shall be forever, where parting shall be no more, and where love, pure love, shall be the ruling passion in, through and by Christ Jesus, and His sacrifice.

Grandaddy and I left the old dogtrot cabin and walked back toward the big house. I didn't feel like hunting any more that day, and old Snaps seemed to sense it as he ambled along at our feet all the way back home.

194

TITHES OF BLOOD

*   *   *

That was many years ago. The old house, called Sunnyside, is gone, a victim of the vicissitudes of time, and the cold, impersonal scalpel of a bulldozer blade. It's all gone - my tree house, the old smokehouse, the warm old kitchen, the feather beds, the old folks, the love and dreams that chink the walls of a country home. I go back occasionally, when the Lord calls another family soul back to the limestone clay of Noxubee County. As the preacher intones, "'Dust unto dust, and to the dust returneth," my eyes stray to the large granite marker in our family plot. The inscription simply reads "T. J. Wilkins, Co. E, 11th Mississippi."

Bravery and love are all the consolation we need.

11th Mississippi
Gettysburg Roster

The 11th Mississippi, with its ten companies and members of its Regimental staff, had present for the Pickett/Pettigrew charge on the 3rd of July, 1863, at the Battle of Gettysburg a minimum of 386 men. Casualties of the Regiment were: killed - died of wounds, 110; wounded, wounded and captured, 187; and captured, unwounded, 39; a total of 336. All these casualties, except two killed and perhaps a few wounded during the cannonading that preceded the charge, were sustained in less than two hours. The total casualties of the 11th Mississippi Regiment amounted to an astounding eighty-seven percent of the aggregate present on the field of battle which was the highest casualties of any regiment, North or South, that fought at Gettysburg.

TITHES OF BLOOD

Company casualties were as follows:

Company A - the University Greys

Aggregate in battle	35
Killed	12
Wounded	23
Casualty rate	100%

Killed
William O'Brien, Regimental Staff

James E. Ballard	William H. Cochran
Samuel M. Brewer	W. T. Estes
Franklin Oliver Dailey	Jeremiah S. Gage
William R. Hall	Robert W. Goodwin
Thomas Heslep	William Augustus Raines
Thomas F. McKie	

Wounded - Wounded and Captured

James H. Dailey	James W. Hale
Albert T. Myers	James C. Taylor
Joshua C. Taylor	Edward L. Harris
Almouth B. Heslep	Rufus P. Heslep
Charles A. Hicks	William J. Hurt
John H. Ivy	James A. Jones
James J. King	Willis M. Lea

11TH MISSISSIPPI ROSTER

Joseph L. McKie
Calvin R. Myers
Andrew J. Baker
Richard C. Bridges
James A. Smith

Jonathan V. Moore
Hugh Q. Bridges
Needham J. Dabney
W. Fort DeGraffenreid

TITHES OF BLOOD

Company B - the Coahoma Invincibles

Aggregate in battle   39
    Killed   11
    Wounded   11
    Captured, unwounded   5
    Escaped, unwounded
Casualty rate   70%

Killed

Robert A. Crenshaw   Louis A. Lawrence
William M. Maynard   Thomas D. Musgraves
Elisha N. Richardson   Hopkins R. Richardson
Akana McHenry   William D. Nun
Benjamin A. Sims   Archibald P. Matthews
William Wright

Wounded - captured

James T. Bartley   John S. T. Grubbs
James S. Haynes   George W. Hurst
Henry C. McLeod   J. F. McLeod
Charles E. Maynard   Henry C. Montroy
George W. Morton   William W. Ward
James C. Henders

Captured - unwounded

Council C. Canfield   Eldridge H. St. John
Jonathan J. Ashe   Johathan R. Garner
Jonathan Sanquinette

11TH MISSISSIPPI ROSTER

Company C - The Prairie Rifles

Aggregate in battle	29
Killed - died of wounds	6
Wounded	17
Captured, unwounded	1
Casualty rate	83%

Killed

Eli H. Peel

James Kyle

William A. Robinson

George G. Temple

Theophilus R. Davenport

Thomas F. Paramore

Wounded and captured

Benjamin A. Abbot

George F. Cole

Richard S. Davidson

George Kidd

Green Kyle

Thomas J. Biddlebroks

James M. Parchman

James T. Ponder

Franklin G. Thomas

Marion P. Bond

Ashley B. Crumpton

George W. Justice

Abraham Klause

George M. Lusher

Jonathan Morris

William H. Peel

George W. Shannon

Captured - unwounded

William H. Smith

TITHES OF BLOOD

Company D - the Neshoba Rifles

Aggregate in battle	55
Killed	11
Wounded	28
Captured, unwounded	7
Escaped, unwounded	10
Casualty rate	84%

Killed

Samuel Y. Boydston

Thomas J. Cooper

Miles M. Rikard

J. Amos Thornell

William J. Brown

T. J. Richardson

Columbus M. Cook

Wayne C. Harrison

John W. Shepard

Joshua Threatt

Jonathan Birmingham

Wounded

Jonathan R. Prince

James A. Hester

William D. Jones

Albert G. Johnson

George Y. Morrell

John L. Rawls

Eli Seale

James H. Bassett

Henry T. Hester

Randall M. Mayo

Archibald M. McDonald

Andrew J. McDonald

David L. Pigg

Charles A. Ridout

Hardy Williamson

Daniel C. Bates

11TH MISSISSIPPI ROSTER

Jacob H. Cook

Thomas M. Cook

Jonathan W. Cook

David W. Copeland

Hiram P. Harrison

Joseph T. Brown

William H. Ferguson

Solomon Edwards

Jesse S. Gully

Wiley P. Heflin

Hampton J. Herrington

John A. Stovall

TITHES OF BLOOD

Company E - the Prairie Guards

Aggregate in battle	38
Killed	14
Wounded	23
Escaped, unwounded	1
Casualty rate	97%

Killed

David C. Wilkins	Henry P. Halbert
Henry M. Wilkins	Jonathan T. Jones
George W. Edwards	Thomas P. Mimms
J. Leander Huckaby	John W. Ball
John R. Mimms	Pleasant Goolsby
William A. Allen	Fletcher S. Norwood
Thomas Carr	Liberty S. Martin

Wounded

Thomas J. Wilkins (Narrator)

Wiliam H. Belton	Jefferson L. Edmonds
Artemus J. Ervin	Alexander J. Halbert
Jonathan C. Halbert	William O. Jones
Jehu Kirksey	James D. Love
Jonathan C. Love	James C. Morhead
David S. Turner	Thomas M. Powell
Walter W. Scales	John L. Sherman
Henry B. Tharp	Thomas B. Moorhead

11TH MISSISSIPPI ROSTER

Jonathan W. Turner

John H. White

Jonathan K. Woods

Thomas A. Walker

Maxmiliam Williams

Jonathan W. White

Escaped Unwounded

John Morgan

Company F - the Noxubee Rifles

Aggregate in battle	42
Killed - died of wounds	10
Wounded	30
Captured - unwounded	1
Escaped - unwounded	1
Casualty rate	97%

Killed

Adoniram J. Farmer	Augustus A. Greer
William F. Hardy	Bernard Mahorner
Harris Mahorner	Daniel A. Featherston
Joseph R. Pendleton	Richard R. Pierce
Robert D. Sanders	Charles J. Stewart

Wounded - captured

Samuel M. Bowen	Charles O. Brooks
John A. Dorroh	Laban T. Freeman
Jonathan L. Holt	Franklin J. M. Lewis
James T. L. Jones	Jonathan A. Jones
Frank A. Howell	Alexander W. Maneese
William C. Nance	Asa B. Robinson
Ira A. Russell	Thomas J. Shaw
Thomas J. Stokes	Erasmus A. Thomas
Elbert H. Thompson	Richard C. White
John J. Howell	Absolom H. Gavin
Francis M. Hill	Oliver H. P. Windham

11TH MISSISSIPPI ROSTER

James W. Hughes

Newton L. Wood

Francis A. Moore

John J. Vincent

James T. Jones

Hiram J. Binion

Rienzi Mahorner

Jonathan C. Williams

TITHES OF BLOOD

Company G - the Lamar Rifles

Aggregate in battle	24
Killed - died of wounds	5
Wounded	15
Escaped, unwounded	4
Casualty rate	83%

Killed

Parham M. Buford   Dudley A. Isom

Newton R. Wilkins   Wesley A. Hyde

William A. Osborne

Wounded

John R. Barry   Robert F. Dickens

Henry G. Fernandez   Charles W. Harris

Jonathan W. Morrow   Wiliam G. Nelms

Ira B. Orr   Thomas H. Wilson

Robert H. Wyatt   James W. Biggers

John F. Brown   James B. Stowers

Theordore C. Burney   Isaac W. Lieterbee

James F. Dooley

11TH MISSISSIPPI ROSTER

Company H - the Chickasaw Guards

Aggregate in battle	40
Killed - died of wounds	12
Wounded	18
Captured, unwounded	7
Escaped, unwounded	3
Casualty rate	92%

Killed

William A. Barton	John V. Harris
William H. Marable	William P. Marion
Mordecai J. Murphy	Abiah E. Robertson
George T. Shaw	Francis P. Hamilton
Thomas W. Hill	Robert N. Lyon
Jamison H. Moore	David N. Smith

Wounded - captured

Thomas J. Boatner	Thomas V. Gordon
James M. Griffin	William R. Holland
W. Pendleton Knox	George N. Lee
James L. Lyon	William B. McDowell
Robert B. Marion	Robert K. Marion
William T. Moore	Lemuel N. Reid
Warren D. Reid	James L. Roberson
Joseph M. Smith	Samuel L. Wilson
John C. Wright	George M. Mathis

TITHES OF BLOOD

Captured - unwounded

Samuel R. Carothers	Thomas J. Holliday
Samuel Reid	Jonathan S. Marable
Joseph G. Marable	Robert A. McDowell

11TH MISSISSIPPI ROSTER

Company I - the Van Dorn Reserves

Aggregate in battle	45
Killed - died of wounds	9
Wounded	24
Captured - unwounded	1
Escaped, unwounded	1
Casualty rate	76%

Killed

James T. Conway	William Awalt
Isaac G. Bell	Thomas A. Gilmer
Wiliam H. Lyle	Charles Strong
Luceillus S. Burnett	Lycurgus W. Morgan
Beverly D. Young	

Wounded - captured

Lucius B. Beale	Nathaniel R. Davidson
William H. Clopton	James D. Demoville
George W. Elkin	James M. Gillespie
James B. Gladney	Wiliam H. Gladney
Joseph L. King	Joseph B. McAllister
Norman T. McKay	William J. McNairy
William H. Meek	Patrick J. Mulvihill
Richard C. Sartor	Jonathan B. Sims
Walton P. Snowden	George W. Wall
Alexander S. Word	William B. Word
James S. Boothe	Tranquillus A. C. Mann
Thomas C. Shell	Eugene C. Turbeville

TITHES OF BLOOD

Company K - the Carroll County Rifles

Aggregate in battle   38
    Killed - died of wounds   10
    Wounded   18
    Captured - unwounded   5
    Escaped, unwounded   7
Casualty rate   86%

Killed

John T. Johnston	Elisha L. Lee
George W. Bird	Josiah E. Boatwright
Nathaniel A. Clark	Jonathan M. Durham
James Cobb	Joseph W. Liddell
Thomas J. Roach	James A. Shackelford

Captured - wounded

John W. Jennings	Alexander L. Kimbrough
Alfred Jones	James H. Kimbrough
DeWitt C. Lee	Thomas A. Kimbrough
William B. Marshall	George W. Oury
Thomas F. Oury	Jonathan W. Shackelford
Elijah H. Spencer	Jonathan T. Stanford
Green A. Williams	Marshall W. H. Stevens
Albert G. Drake	Samuel J. Harper
Daniel O. Ross	John T. Standley

Captured - unwounded

Rhesa R. Hawkins	Duncan McRae
Henry Moores	Archibald J. Turner
Henry C. Royal	

Regimental Staff

Aggregate in battle   5
    Killed - died of wounds   1
    Wounded   3
    Escaped - unwounded   1
Casualty rate   80%

Killed
William O'Brien

Wounded - wounded and captured
Francis M. Green   Thomas C. Holliday
Reuben O. Reynolds

The Eleventh, with a total of 336 casualties, had greater casualties than any of the fifteen regiments of Pickett's division. When viewed on a casualty rate basis (casualties to total present), none suffered greater that the 11th Mississippi with an eighty-seven percent loss rate.

High Tide at Gettysburg

by Will Henry Thompson

Then at the brief command of Lee
    moved out that matchless infantry,
with Pickett leading grandly down,
    to charge against that roaring crown
of those dread heights of destiny.

Far above the angry guns
    a cry across the tumult runs,
The voice that rang through Shiloh's woods
    and Chickamauga's solitudes,
The fierce South cheering on her sons!

Oh, how the withering tempest blew
    against the front of Pettigrew;
A Khamsin wind that scorched and singed
    like that infernal flame that fringed
The British squares at Waterloo!

A thousand fell where Kemper led;
    A thousand died where Garnett bled,
In blinding flame and strangling smoke
    the remnant through the batteries broke
and crossed the works with Armisted.

TITHES OF BLOOD

In vain did Mississippi set,
    her breast against the bayonet,
In vain her bravest charged and raged,
    A tigress in her wrath uncaged,
Till all the hill was red and wet!

Once more in Glory's van with me!
    Virginia cried to Tennessee,
we two together, come what may,
    Shall stand upon those works today,
The reddest day in history!

Brave Tennessee, in reckless way
    Virginia heard her comrade say,
Close round this rent and riddled Rag,
    in time she set that battle flag,
Amid the guns of Doubleday!

But who shall break the guards that wait
    Before the awful face of fate?
The tattered standards of the South,
    Were shriveled at the cannon's mouth
And all her hopes were desolate.

They fell, who lifted up a hand
    and bade the sun in heaven to stand;
They smote and fell, who set the bars,
    Against the progress of the stars
And stayed the march of Motherland!

The brave went down without disgrace
    They leaped to ruin's red embrace;
They only heard fame's thunders wake
    And saw the dazling sun-burst break
in smiles on Glory's bloody face.

TITHES OF BLOOD

"The Returned Battle Flags."

───────────────

By Mrs. Eron Gregory
Assistant Curator
Mississippi Department of Archives and History.

───────────────

1905

Oh, not with gayly spreading folds,
    And colors fresh and bright,
They fling their gleaming stars and bars,
    Triumphant, to the light;

But sadly 'round their broken staffs,
    They droop in faded folds,
Their service o'er, their duty done,
    Their wondrous story told.

Upon their wreck the warrior aged,
    Looks long, with moistened eye,
Caressing each worn fold, the while
    Is heard his heavy sigh.

Once more he sees the gleaming host,
    That pressed with fearless tread,
Toward the heights of liberty,
    With its countless dead

And never pennon streamed above
A rank, more fair than the,
Bright ensigns of that proud grey host
Of Robert Edmund Lee.

To-day, with flowers springing where
War's crimson currents ran,
And peace and love now reign above
The splendor of our land,

These furled and silent banners stir
No sad regret or pain,
We read our fairest history in
The story of their fame

ANV Battleflag of the 11th Mississippi Infantry Regiment

Inscription on the Confederate Monument
Brooksville, Mississippi

-Our Heroes - 1861-1865

Love's tribute to the noble men who marched 'neath the
Flag of Stars and Bars and were faithful to the end.

God of our fathers help us to preserve for our children,
the priceless treasure of the true story of the Confederate
Soldiers.

Post Script

Material is not at hand to give a full account of the prison experiences of members of "The Prairie Guards" and the 11th Mississippi Regiment. It would be a dark page and one by no means complimentary to the professed Christianity and enlightenment of the age. There are some, to this day, who are preaching forgetfulness of the past, but the descendents of the Prairie Guards and the 11th Mississippi are not ashamed of their past. No stone, however humble, marks the resting place of many of its members who fell. They sleep in unknown graves in the swamps of the Chickahominy; in the thickets of the wilderness; on the broad plateau of Manassas; at Sharpsburg, at Gettysburg. Their names do not illumine the historic page, but they are not yet forgotten and their proud descendants and the 11th Mississippi Memorial Committee plan to remember their bravery and sacrifice, and honor their memory for generations to come.